COPING WITH SCHIZO

DR STEVEN JONES is a clinical p
at the Institute of Psychiatry and the Maudsley Hospital, London. His clinical work concentrates on people with long-term mental health problems, the majority having a diagnosis of schizophrenia. He has also been researching into the psychological aspects of schizophrenia and related disorders over the past nine years. This work has been published in a number of international academic journals.

DR FRANK TALLIS, also a chartered clinical psychologist, practises at the South Kensington and Chelsea Mental Health Centre, the Chelsea and Westminster Hospital, London. In the past he has worked as a counsellor for organizations such as MIND and MENCAP and has been a lecturer in psychology at the Institute of Psychiatry and King's College, London. He has worked extensively with individuals with schizophrenia, especially those with concurrent anxiety problems. He has published articles in international journals on a wide range of topics and is the author of *How to Stop Worrying* and *Understanding Obsessions and Compulsions* both published by Sheldon Press.

Overcoming Common Problems Series

For a full list of titles please contact
Sheldon Press, Marylebone Road, London NW1 4DU

The Assertiveness Workbook
A plan for busy women
JOANNA GUTMANN

Birth Over Thirty
SHEILA KITZINGER

Body Language
How to read others' thoughts by their gestures
ALLAN PEASE

Body Language in Relationships
DAVID COHEN

Calm Down
How to cope with frustration and anger
DR PAUL HAUCK

Changing Course
How to take charge of your career
SUE DYSON AND STEPHEN HOARE

Comfort for Depression
JANET HORWOOD

Coping Successfully with Agoraphobia
DR KENNETH HAMBLY

Coping Successfully with Migraine
SUE DYSON

Coping Successfully with Pain
NEVILLE SHONE

Coping Successfully with Panic Attacks
SHIRLEY TRICKETT

Coping Successfully with Prostate Problems
ROSY REYNOLDS

Coping Successfully with Your Hyperactive Child
DR PAUL CARSON

Coping Successfully with Your Irritable Bowel
ROSEMARY NICOL

Coping Successfully with Your Second Child
FIONA MARSHALL

Coping with Anxiety and Depression
SHIRLEY TRICKETT

Coping with Blushing
DR ROBERT EDELMANN

Coping with Cot Death
SARAH MURPHY

Coping with Depression and Elation
DR PATRICK McKEON

Coping with Strokes
DR TOM SMITH

Coping with Suicide
DR DONALD SCOTT

Coping with Thrush
CAROLINE CLAYTON

Curing Arthritis Diet Book
MARGARET HILLS

Curing Arthritis – The Drug-Free Way
MARGARET HILLS

Curing Arthritis
More ways to a drug-free life
MARGARET HILLS

Curing Coughs, Colds and Flu – The Drug-Free Way
MARGARET HILLS

Curing Illness – The Drug-Free Way
MARGARET HILLS

Depression
DR PAUL HAUCK

Divorce and Separation
Every woman's guide to a New Life
ANGELA WILLANS

Don't Blame Me!
How to stop blaming yourself and other people
TONY GOUGH

Everything You Need to Know about Shingles
DR ROBERT YOUNGSON

Family First Aid and Emergency Handbook
DR ANDREW STANWAY

Overcoming Common Problems Series

Fight Your Phobia and Win
DAVID LEWIS

Getting Along with People
DIANNE DOUBTFIRE

Getting Married
JOANNA MOORHEAD

Getting the Best for your Bad Back
DR ANTHONY CAMPBELL

Goodbye Backache
DR DAVID IMRIE WITH COLLEEN DIMSON

Heart Attacks – Prevent and Survive
DR TOM SMITH

Helping Children Cope with Divorce
ROSEMARY WELLS

Helping Children Cope with Grief
ROSEMARY WELLS

Helping Children Cope with Stress
URSULA MARKHAM

Hold Your Head Up High
DR PAUL HAUCK

How to Be Your Own Best Friend
DR PAUL HAUCK

How to Cope with Splitting Up
VERA PEIFFER

How to Cope with Stress
DR PETER TYRER

How to Cope with Tinnitus and Hearing Loss
DR ROBERT YOUNGSON

How to Do What You Want to Do
DR PAUL HAUCK

How to Improve Your Confidence
DR KENNETH HAMBLY

How to Interview and Be Interviewed
MICHELE BROWN AND GYLES BRANDRETH

How to Love and be Loved
DR PAUL HAUCK

How to Negotiate Successfully
PATRICK FORSYTH

How to Pass Your Driving Test
DONALD RIDLAND

How to Solve Your Problems
BRENDA ROGERS

How to Spot Your Child's Potential
CECILE DROUIN AND ALAIN DUBOS

How to Stand up for Yourself
DR PAUL HAUCK

How to Start a Conversation and Make Friends
DON GABOR

How to Stop Smoking
GEORGE TARGET

How to Stop Worrying
DR FRANK TALLIS

How to Survive Your Teenagers
SHEILA DAINOW

How to Untangle Your Emotional Knots
DR WINDY DRYDEN AND JACK GORDON

Hysterectomy
SUZIE HAYMAN

Is HRT Right for You?
DR ANNE MACGREGOR

The Incredible Sulk
DR WINDY DRYDEN

The Irritable Bowel Diet Book
ROSEMARY NICOL

The Irritable Bowel Stress Book
ROSEMARY NICOL

Jealousy
DR PAUL HAUCK

Learning from Experience
A woman's guide to getting older without panic
PATRICIA O'BRIEN

Learning to Live with Multiple Sclerosis
DR ROBERT POVEY, ROBIN DOWIE AND GILLIAN PRETT

Living Through Personal Crisis
ANN KAISER STEARNS

Living with Grief
DR TONY LAKE

Overcoming Common Problems Series

Living with High Blood Pressure
DR TOM SMITH

Loneliness
DR TONY LAKE

Making Marriage Work
DR PAUL HAUCK

Making the Most of Loving
GILL COX AND SHEILA DAINOW

Making the Most of Yourself
GILL COX AND SHEILA DAINOW

Making Time Work for You
An inner guide to time management
MAREK GITLIN

Managing Two Careers
PATRICIA O'BRIEN

Meeting People is Fun
DR PHYLLIS SHAW

Menopause
RAEWYN MACKENZIE

The Nervous Person's Companion
DR KENNETH HAMBLY

Overcoming Fears and Phobias
DR TONY WHITEHEAD

Overcoming Shyness
A woman's guide
DIANNE DOUBTFIRE

Overcoming Stress
DR VERNON COLEMAN

Overcoming Tension
DR KENNETH HAMBLY

Overcoming Your Nerves
DR TONY LAKE

The Parkinson's Disease Handbook
DR RICHARD GODWIN-AUSTEN

Say When!
Everything a woman needs to know about alcohol and drinking problems
ROSEMARY KENT

Self-defence for Everyday
Practical safety for women and men
PADDY O'BRIEN

Slay Your Own Dragons
How women can overcome self-sabotage in love and work
NANCY GOOD

Sleep Like a Dream – The Drug-Free Way
ROSEMARY NICOL

A Special Child in the Family
Living with your sick or disabled child
DIANA KIMPTON

Stop Smoking
BEN WICKS

Talking About Anorexia
How to cope with life without starving
MAROUSHKA MONRO

Talking About Miscarriage
SARAH MURPHY

Think Your Way to Happiness
DR WINDY DRYDEN AND JACK GORDON

Trying to Have a Baby?
Overcoming infertility and child loss
MAGGIE JONES

Understanding Obsessions and Compulsions
A self-help manual
DR FRANK TALLIS

Understanding Your Personality
Myers-Briggs and More
PATRICIA HEDGES

Vasectomy and Sterlization
Making the right decision
SUZIE HAYMAN

A Weight Off Your Mind
How to stop worrying about your body size
SUE DYSON

Why Be Afraid?
DR PAUL HAUCK

You and Your Varicose Veins
DR PATRICIA GILBERT

You Want Me to Do *What?*
A guide to persuasive communication
PATRICK FORSYTH

Overcoming Common Problems

COPING WITH SCHIZOPHRENIA

Dr Steven Jones and
Dr Frank Tallis

First published in Great Britain in 1994
Sheldon Press, SPCK, Marylebone Road, London NW1 4DU

British Library Cataloguing-in-Publication Data
A catalogue record for this book is available from the British Library

ISBN 0–85969–679–0

Photoset by Deltatype Ltd, Ellesmere Port, Cheshire
Printed in Great Britain by Biddles Ltd, Guildford and King's Lynn

Contents

Foreword

The abnormal behaviours and experiences which result in a diagnosis of schizophrenia are still not well understood, despite considerable progress in recent years. In many ways, this is not surprising since certain of the core disturbances represent fundamental changes in the way an individual experiences the world. Clearly the question of how an idea becomes 'conscious' is both one of the most intriguing, yet puzzling, to philosophers and scientists.

However, it is increasingly apparent that, regardless of the cause of the disorder, the patient and his or her family do not need to remain passive in the face of the difficulties encountered. While not denying that these problems may sometimes be very severe, this book indicates clearly that the most positive outcome is likely to be achieved by a collaboration between the professional staff involved, the patient, and his or her family. Such an approach may decrease the likelihood of relapse, reduce distress, and minimize disabilities.

For this collaboration to work successfully, the patient and his or her family must be helped to understand the nature of the disturbance and the rationale behind the treatments proposed. Recent research has emphasized the utility of the 'educational' component when treatment is to be carried out. The authors make this point very clearly in chapter 3.

This book emphasizes a flexible approach to intervention, with pharmacological and psychological approaches usually being complementary. For some patients psychological treatment may not be possible until medication has had time to effect a partial recovery. This may be particularly so for certain of the newer treatment approaches, such as cognitive therapy, which are outlined in chapter 4.

Ideally, this approach should be employed as a basis for discussion between therapist, family and patient. It will remove some of the misconceptions and reduce anxiety and feelings of loss of control. This book has the virtue of ranging widely over the areas which are of concern to both the patient and his or her family. Issues such as health, hygiene and personal relationships clearly merit equal consideration to those concerning a patient's response to abnormal experiences.

Clearly, during times of disturbance, a patient is unlikely to be able to make use of this book, although his or her family will almost certainly benefit. However, by incorporating an educational component during periods when the patient is partially recovered, the therapist may encourage a gradual change in the patient's insight into, and attitudes to, his difficulties.

For many patients and their families, the most distressing aspect of their illness may not be the hallucinations or delusions. Rather, it is the uncertainty about the future, the disruption of career plans, and difficulties with interpersonal relationships which can lead to feelings of hopelessness. The information conveyed in the pages that follow will go some way to reducing these feelings. The message is a clear one: a diagnosis of schizophrenia does not mean that a patient cannot lead a fulfilling and worthwhile life. Nor is it a condition over which a patient and his family have no control. It is in the end a more optimistic message than thirty years ago. We must hope that the present intensive programme of research into the disorder will make it even more so by the end of the century.

David R. Hemsley
Professor of Abnormal Psychology

Introduction

This book is intended to provide information on the nature of schizophrenia and on treatments which are available for it. It is aimed at people suffering from the illness and at their relatives and friends. As well as identifying traditional medical treatments we set out ways in which people can help themselves. It should be noted from the outset that our intention is not to suggest that a self-help approach is sufficient on its own, but that taking more responsibility for one's treatment can be a useful and important complement to standard care.

Schizophrenia can be a devastating condition affecting not only the sufferer but also his or her friends or relatives. Unfortunately it is often difficult to obtain clear information about the nature of schizophrenia and its consequences. In the first few chapters we therefore try to describe symptoms of schizophrenia, their possible origins and available treatments. Traditional treatments discussed include medication, with information on both benefits and possible side-effects. We also describe a number of non-drug treatments, such as family therapy, which have been shown to have additional benefits.

In chapter 4 a number of relatively new treatment approaches are discussed. Research to date indicates that these techniques have promise for people suffering for schizophrenia. However, it is too early to say for certain precisely how much each individual will gain from each specific technique. Our impression, from experience with our own patients, is that psychological approaches can be very helpful and can be readily adapted to suit individual needs.

The second half of the book concentrates on dealing with a wide range of common problems, including stress, anxiety, anger, money, housing and forming relationships. A number of suggestions are made to help cope with these and related issues. A final section focuses on legal matters, knowing your rights and on ways of getting your views across to people who can help.

1
What is Schizophrenia?

When schizophrenia was first discovered there was really nothing in the way of medical treatement available for sufferers. People with schizophrenia would either be tolerated in their community or, when they became too disruptive, were placed in hospitals or sanatoria, the quality of care usually depending on the wealth of the person's family. The outlook for the individual was bleak and uncertain.

Psychiatry is still a relatively young branch of medicine and although reports of psychotic illness can be found in the earliest writings it was not until the 1900s that the term schizophrenia came to be used.

Before this, major psychiatric illnesses other than depression or anxiety were called 'primary insanity'. The diagnosis of schizophrenia has been refined over the years and there is now much agreement about the crucial features of a schizophrenic breakdown. This agreement has in part been due to the large-scale studies undertaken by international bodies such as the World Health Organization drawing on the expertise of scientists and doctors worldwide.

There are a number of features which are commonly found in schizophrenia, although people with the diagnosis of schizophrenia can differ quite widely. Some people will display all the possible symptoms listed, whereas others may only have a couple of them.

Symptoms of schizophrenia

Hallucinations

A hallucination can occur in any of the senses: hearing, sight, taste, smell or touch. The most common hallucinations in schizophrenia are hearing (or auditory) hallucinations. These auditory hallucinations commonly involve hearing voices of people talking to each other about the person suffering from schizophrenia. They may also speak directly to him/her. Other people hear noises rather than voices; these can be of anything from mechanical noises to the sounds of wind rustling leaves.

John

John has had a schizophrenic illness since he was twenty years old and suffers from hallucinations. He hears the voices of two ghosts who tell him about life after death. He can become very absorbed in these descriptions to the point of not leaving his house for days on end. John quite enjoys these conversations and says he even feels comforted by them at times. However he also hears the voice of a policeman who once arrested him when he was unwell. This voice tells him that he is worthless and will be punished. Quite understandably John finds this voice very upsetting and in the past has broken down and wept in the street while being harangued by this hallucination. When John is well these voices are less frequent and less distinct. He also tends to feel that they are less real and indeed there are periods when the voices disappear altogether.

Visual hallucinations are the second most frequent hallucinatory experience in schizophrenia. Initially it may appear to the person that things seem particularly bright and distinct before fully formed hallucinations occur. Visual hallucinations may be of specific people or objects, or alternatively the person may see moving shapes or patterns disrupting their normal field of vision.

Simon

Simon's first schizophrenic experience was of a complex visual hallucination. He was sitting up late one night in his flat and began to look closely at the walls of his living room. Gradually he realized that the walls were striped with different coloured lights. As he watched these colours increased in intensity. He also began to see the faces of his parents talking to him from these coloured areas. Some weeks later he began to see objects around his flat that could not have been there. He saw an ermine cloak, a mace and a royal crown. Convinced of the reality of these, he felt he must have become a king. He clothed himself in these objects and strode down the local high street to greet his subjects. He was eventually arrested by the police because he was in fact walking about naked. Several years on from this first incident the objects no longer appear to Simon. Occasionally the coloured stripes will appear but he now concentrates on distracting himself from this by going for a walk, which is usually sufficient to take his mind off them.

Hallucinations of taste, smell and touch are rather less common. In each case, as with visual and auditory hallucinations, the experiences can range from the pleasant to the terrifying. Taste hallucinations are often concerned with food or drink that has been tampered with or poisoned. This can be very distressing both for the sufferer and for their relatives as the person may eventually refuse to eat for fear of poisoning. These experiences usually respond to treatment, allowing the person to eat and drink with less fear.

Delusions

A delusion is a fixed and bizarre belief in something in the face of evidence which would usually convince someone else that it is false.

The person with schizophrenia will often feel persecuted, believing that people are conspiring behind his or her back to harm him or her. It will often seem as though everyday occurrences (such as an item of news or the number plate of a car) hold special significance and may be further evidence of their persecution. In the acute stages of schizophrenia many individuals believe that their thoughts are interfered with. This may be because they can be heard by others, because other people's thoughts are being inserted into the mind of the person with schizophrenia, or because thoughts are being taken out of their mind against their will.

Karen

Karen's first schizophrenic breakdown occurred when she was 23 years old. She began to withdraw and avoid contact with family and friends. She neglected her job and spent most of her time watching television. She felt that the television news reports contained coded signals to her which informed her when the world would come to an end. When these were particularly forceful she would become very upset and attempt to contact the government so that they could alert everyone else to this problem. She felt that these messages came to her because she had been 'chosen' by a higher power. Some of her thoughts also felt as though they had been placed there by this power to guide her in her life. Karen eventually agreed to seek help when she lost her job (for non-attendance over the previous four weeks) some three months after these delusions first began.

Reduced motivation

In the face of all of the above experiences the person suffering from schizophrenia is left feeling perplexed and unsure of who they are as a person. Whereas in the past they may have had particular aims and desires these can often seem irrelevant or pointless to them following the onset of the illness.

A common complaint from the carers of people with schizophrenia is that they are lazy: they do not show any interest in anything, they just won't get going. Schizophrenia does make even the simplest of everyday activities (washing, grooming, getting up in the morning) more difficult than people who have not experienced the disorder imagine. The reasons for this can vary. In the early stages of schizophrenia some people find that reducing their level of activity to a bare minimum can lead to some relief from hallucinations and delusions. Although drug treatments for schizophrenia can help with the hallucinations, they can themselves make people feel tired and listless if dosages are not correctly adjusted. In addition, basic motivation to engage in such activities can be reduced by the illness process. It can be of great assistance to family members to understand that what appears to be laziness in the person with schizophrenia is often part of the illness process itself, rather than a wilful act.

Social skills

The term social skills refers to the manner in which we communicate with other people. Socially skilled individuals use tone of voice, physical gestures, eye contact and posture to help them communicate effectively with other people and to give a good impression.

Social skills can be impaired in schizophrenia. People may find it difficult to string together all the different aspects of a skilful social interaction. This will be partly because of motivational problems, as above. However, the interference from delusional beliefs and hallucinations also contribute to social skills difficulties. In the short term, hearing voices is distracting and means that it is hard to give your attention to the conversation which you might be engaged in. If in addition you believe that the person is attempting to interfere with your mind, or intends to harm you, you will be unlikely to make normal eye contact or open encouraging gestures to the person. If these difficulties continue over a long period then the normal range of social skills can become impaired, even when the level of hallucinations and delusions is reduced. In such situations it may be necessary for the person to take social skills training to relearn some of the skills that have either been lost or become rusty with under use.

Everyday life skills

These are the skills which the individual needs to take care of themselves and avoid exploitation when living independently in the community. Except in the most severe forms of schizophrenic breakdown, people retain the ability to clothe, wash and eat. However, it is not uncommon for people when they are becoming ill to let their standards of dress and personal hygiene drop below those maintained when they are well. Other important living skills are the ability to manage money and to read and write. Difficulty in managing money can again be a potent source of conflict with carers. Many people with schizophrenia do this perfectly well, but it can be a problem for some. This can either be due to any illness-related difficulty in understanding the value of money or due to delusional beliefs (e.g. I am a king/queen) that tell the person they have no need to take care of money as it will not run out. Literacy among people with schizophrenia is very similar to that in the general population, but can be impaired when the person becomes ill; they may then need direct help to complete forms or write letters.

It is easy to see that the apparent feeling of power and insight which can go along with the early stages of schizophrenia can lead to neglect of the everyday routines engaged in by the rest of the world. If you are busy decoding messages from a super being or listening to villains plotting your downfall you will not want to be bothered with sorting out bills or shopping for food or even regular washing. These activities take second place to the overwhelming importance of the psychotic experience.

Tasks that were previously easily accomplished become burdensome and difficult. Work activities and hobbies which were previously interesting can become viewed as boring, frustrating and pointless.

It is difficult for somebody with schizophrenia to maintain normal relationships with others when they are suffering from the symptoms described above. How can you talk and act normally with work colleagues when you believe they are involved in a sinister plot to kill you? How can you concentrate on a conversation when someone in your head is talking about something completely different? It is therefore very common for people to withdraw from society, particularly in the early stages of schizophrenia, seeing only a few people, often close family members. In the short term this can reduce the severity of the symptoms. However, if continued over long periods of time, it can lead to feeling permanently alienated and different from others, even when the hallucinations and delusions have become less severe.

As will be discussed in later chapters, the person with schizophrenia has difficult decisions to make about the appropriate level of contact with the outside world. It is often the case that a moderate degree of withdrawal from social contact can be an appropriate way to reduce feelings of over-arousal and distress, but this needs to be balanced by the positive effects of involvement with friends and family and the support and help they can provide.

Different types of schizophrenia

As discussed above, the symptoms of schizophrenia are varied and two people with the same diagnosis may in practice experience it differently. There are a number of additional psychiatric terms which are commonly associated with a diagnosis of schizophrenia which it is useful to be aware of.

Paranoid schizophrenia is so called because the person's hallucinations and delusions largely focus on one theme which is often related to a belief that they will be harmed, attacked, threatened, abused or killed. A non-paranoid diagnosis indicates that such experiences do not focus primarily on one theme.

Acute and *chronic* are two other terms which are commonly used. A diagnosis of acute schizophrenia indicates that the person has only had the illness for a short period of time (normally six months to two years); if it extends beyond this period it is chronic. One possible source of confusion here is that the term acute can also be used to indicate that a person who had been well (in remission) has begun to experience hallucinations and delusions again and has become in need of more intensive treatment.

Alcohol and drug use

People in the early stages of schizophrenia may consume alcohol as a means of reducing the interference experienced from voices and disturbing thoughts. In the short term, alcohol does have immediate effects, but in addition to the risk of dependency it can make worse the very experiences from which the person is trying to escape. When an individual has access to adequate treatment their symptoms will usually improve and the need for alcohol as an alternative 'medication' will tend to reduce. There are some people with schizophrenia who are alcohol dependent, but this is not common.

Some people with schizophrenia use cannabis on a regular basis. They often feel that this helps with sleep and makes them feel calm.

In addition to the question of its illegality, however, it is associated with a worsening of symptoms in a number of studies of people with schizophrenia and is therefore to be avoided.

Use of other 'street' drugs (such as cocaine and heroin) is no more common in people with schizophrenia than it is in other areas of the population.

How common is schizophrenia?

Schizophrenia is much more common than many people would think. Up to one in every hundred people is likely to have, or have had, a diagnosis of schizophrenia at some point in their lives. This means that in a street of twenty family houses, at least one resident would be schizophrenic. Far from being a disorder which happens to the very few, most people will know of someone who is schizophrenic, even if they are not aware of the person's diagnosis. It used to be thought that schizophrenia was best treated by removing the sufferer from the stress and strains of everyday life and placing them in a hospital. There they would be cared for until they were sufficiently recovered to return to society. Although hospitalization can be helpful in the short term for some people, most people who have a diagnosis of schizophrenia live most of their lives in the community. This may mean living with family, in hostels, or independently in their own property. Wherever the person lives they will come into contact with many people during their day who have no idea of their diagnosis and indeed there is no reason why they should know. As with any other group of human beings, the abilities of each individual sufferer will be different. The role of professional and self help should be to help that individual reach his or her own potential at whatever level that may be. For some people that will mean having their own home, a demanding job and hobbies; for others it will involve staying out of hospital with help from carers and spending time in a supported environment.

Is schizophrenia more common in men or women?

It seems that the risk of schizophrenia is approximately equal for men and women. However, although the actual numbers of men and women with schizophrenia is the same, the age at which they become ill does tend to differ. In general, men appear to experience their first schizophrenic breakdown at an earlier age than women. It is most common for men to be in their early to mid twenties when they first come into contact with mental health services for this sort of problem. For women, this occurs around ten years later on average.

Do hallucinations or delusions only occur in schizophrenia?

The experience of hallucinations and delusions (see above) extends beyond the group of people suffering from schizophrenia. Within the psychiatric field there are a large number of other disorders in which the person can suffer unusual or disturbing experiences, although usually to a lesser degree and over shorter periods than experienced in schizophrenia. Hallucinations can occur in people withdrawing from alcohol, people who use street drugs, people with severe depression and in diseases that attack parts of the brain (dementia/Alzheimer's disease, brain tumours). A substantial number of people, in addition to those with schizophrenia, will experience some psychotic symptoms, as a result of either drug use or other illness.

More recently there have been investigations of schizophrenic-like symptoms in the general population. 'Schizophrenic-like' means experiences of a similar type to those found in schizophrenia, but less severe. An example would be a feeling of heightened awareness, or the feeling that things look odd; the person with schizophrenia would be convinced that things were odd and had a special meaning for them. It has been found that there are many people who have no psychiatric diagnosis, and who are not receiving medication or abusing drugs, who experience many of these schizophrenic-like symptoms.

If these people have schizophrenic-like symptoms, why do they not become schizophrenic? It has been shown that people who have a lot of these schizophrenic-like experiences are more likely to become schizophrenic than other members of the general population. But it is still only a small minority that do become ill. The majority of such people lead normal lives. They tend to differ from people with schizophrenia in being more able to turn their minds away from unusual experiences when necessary. Thus they are able to concentrate at work or school when required, although they may be more likely to day-dream when not under pressure.

What are the causes of schizophrenia?

In the last few sections we have tried to describe some of the main features that occur in schizophrenia. It is clear that most people with schizophrenia suffer at some time in their illness from experiences which are very different from those who care for or live with them. Why do these bizarre feelings and experiences happen?

This question has preoccupied scientists and clinicians since the development of the term over a hundred years ago. It seems as though there are a number of different factors associated with schizophrenic illness.

Genes and schizophrenia

One of the earliest findings was that schizophrenia tends to run in families. A person with no schizophrenic relatives is very unlikely to suffer a schizophrenic breakdown. However, if one or both parents are schizophrenic this likelihood can increase dramatically. In the early studies the likelihood of developing schizophrenia if both parents had the illness was rated as high as fifty per cent.

Some workers argued that this meant that schizophrenia is largely a genetic illness, genes being the basic biological code which can cause schizophrenia to be passed on from parent to child. Others have said that schizophrenia runs in families because people with schizophrenia have parenting and communication problems which create an environment where further schizophrenic illness is more likely.

More recent work has shown that although genes are important there is much about the development of schizophrenia which they do not explain.

Families and schizophrenia

In the 1950s and 1960s there was a large increase in work with families of people with mental illness. In addition, clinicians made efforts to understand the experience of the person with mental illness and to use this in helping to treat them. This approach had some unfortunate consequences. It was widely suggested at this time that schizophrenia could result from the way in which children were brought up. This in effect led some clinicians to be tempted to blame the family for the developments of a person's illness. This was unhelpful in adding to the distress of family members already likely to be suffering guilt and confusion in the face of the frightening illness.

Although schizophrenia is more common in people who have had disadvantages in their upbringing, this is true for a whole range of illnesses. If a person has to face profound difficulties in early life they are more likely to have problems when adult. These may express themselves in mental illness or drug use or may be redirected into ambition and career drive.

This does not mean however that everyone with schizophrenia has had a difficult childhood, any more than this is true for people with anxiety problems.

It is known now that the family has important roles to play in helping someone with schizophrenia to stay well. This is discussed further in later chapters. But whereas there is good evidence that families can help people with schizophrenia to remain well, it is not the case that families can be blamed for schizophrenia occurring.

The brain and schizophrenia

The brain is the organ through which we think and make sense of what we see, hear, feel, smell and taste. Since all these faculties can be disturbed by schizophrenia it is logical that there should be work to investigate whether there are any problems in the brains of people who have schizophrenia.

Some differences have been reported in the size and shape of the brains of people who have had schizophrenia. However these differences are not large and it is not always clear whether changes are due to the schizophrenic illness itself or to other factors.

Other research has focused on the chemicals which we have in our brains. Since the balance of these is altered by all the drugs which are effective in schizophrenia it may be that people with schizophrenia suffer from an imbalance in such chemicals. In particular, it is known that *dopamine*, one of the chemicals that allows messages to travel around the brain, is reduced by drugs that help schizophrenia. It is therefore possible that schizophrenia results, at least in part, from having too much of this chemical in the brain.

Stress and schizophrenia

Stress seems to be an important factor in schizophrenic illness. People who have schizophrenia tend to have a large number of life events in the month before they become ill for the first time. A 'life event' is anything significant that happens in your life. It could be a positive thing such as marriage, a job promotion or the birth of a child; or it could be a sad or difficult event such as divorce, housing problems or bereavement. People who suffer from depression also tend to have more life events in the periods before they become ill. The difference with schizophrenia is that it does not seem to matter whether the events are positive or negative ones. It seems as though people who are prone to schizophrenia are generally sensitive to stress and that large amounts of this are related to schizophrenic breakdown. This is also true for people who have schizophrenia but are currently well. Increasing numbers of life events are associated with recurrence of the illness. Subsequent chapters discuss how best to deal with stress so that its potentially harmful effects are minimized. In general it is found that people with a reasonably stable network of supportive family and friends who are able to occupy their time in a constructive way are less vulnerable to the effects of life events.

Vulnerability and triggers for schizophrenia

In the preceding sections the roles of genes, families, brain disorder and stress have been discussed in relationship to schizophrenia. Overall it is clear that although each of these can play a role in schizophrenic breakdown none are sufficient on their own. The most widely accepted view is that the majority of people who suffer a schizophrenic illness are predisposed to schizophrenia in earlier life. This predisposition, whether through genes, brain or personality means that the person is vulnerable to schizophrenic breakdown under certain circumstances (usually under stress). A number of different life events (adolescence, marriage, divorce, parenthood) can be a source of stress, as can be conflicts within the family. If the person is strongly predisposed to schizophrenia it only takes a relatively few stressful events to trigger a schizophrenic episode. If, on the other hand, they are less predisposed it will require substantial amounts of stress over a long period for schizophrenia to occur.

How do people get treatment for schizophrenia?

The types and range of treatments which are available for people with schizophrenia will be dealt with in subsequent chapters. A fundamental issue is how to obtain access to these treatments. Traditionally the person who is becoming ill with schizophrenia, or a member of their family, will contact their General Practitioner in the first instance for help. The GP will then either offer treatment themselves or refer the person to specialist mental health services. Referral to specialist psychiatric services is common in the early stages of schizophrenia as the person is likely to require more time and input than many GPs are free to give.

If the person is very acutely ill it may be necessary to obtain hospital admission for initial assessment and treatment by a mental health team. Such admissions are now rarely for longer than a period of a few months, after which treatment tends to be provided in the community. Hospital admission may be requested by the GP or by the patient's family. In the early stages of schizophrenia in particular, the person themselves will rarely request this as they will tend to be convinced of the reality of their abnormal experiences.

How does the Community Care Act affect access to treatments?

The Community Care Act 1991 is having a number of effects on the way people get access to help from health services generally. One of the main effects of this legislation is that local authorities, rather than health services, become responsible for assessing and arranging care for people in need of it. This applies for both mental and general health services.

Assessment for treatment for all illness used to rest mainly with GPs and other medically qualified staff. In practice it is likely that many people will continue to obtain help through this traditional route, although an additional assessment of needs is made by social services as part of this process. People can also now go straight to the social service departments to request an assessment of their needs, which will result in a 'care package' being developed between the social worker responsible for the assessment and the person being assessed. These assessments are also intended to be carried out for people who are admitted to assess their needs on discharge.

The emphasis of the Act, as its name indicates, is on providing alternatives to hospital care. If care is delivered in an efficient way outside hospital to meet the needs of the person with schizophrenia, it is thought that they are less likely to require admission to hospital, and if admission does occur the emphasis will be on it being for as short a time as possible.

The assessment procedure which is part of this Act is conducted by a named social worker and is discussed with the person involved. It is also subject to review and there are appeals and complaints procedures in place for people who feel their needs are not being met.

The precise details of these procedures vary across the country but details are available at local authority offices.

Do people recover from schizophrenia?

Schizophrenia is a serious illness and many early psychiatrists saw little hope for sufferers. They regarded it as a permanent and incurable illness. This is now known to be untrue. After the first schizophrenic breakdown about a third of people will find that symptoms resolve and do not reappear. Around half of the people who have suffered a schizophrenic breakdown will be able to support themselves in work and run their homes with little interference from symptoms over the five years following their illness. For the remaining people schizophrenia appears usually to take a fluctuating course. There will be periods, often extended, when the illness is in remission and other times when symptoms recur and additional treatment is required. As discussed later on, people have a crucial role to play in their own treatment, as do carers. Most people are aware of particular signs to themselves that their problem is worsening and that they may be becoming ill again. Early action taken when these are first noticed can often greatly reduce the severity and duration of any relapse.

Many people who have had a diagnosis of schizophrenia will be able to work and support themselves subsequently. A further group of people will be able to do this most of the time but will have periods when additional support and help is required. It is therefore only a small proportion of people with a schizophrenic illness who require intensive support over long periods of time.

For people who do return to regular work it is common initially to try working in a less demanding position to acclimatize again to the work situation. Some people will eventually find that they can work as hard and fast as they ever did; others will realize that they feel rather more vulnerable to pressure than they did before. In this case it does not mean that work is abandoned, rather that the individual needs to adjust their routine to minimize pressure, which may include taking a less demanding job.

Does schizophrenia mean having a multiple or split personality?

The term 'schizophrenia' has now become part of everyday language and most people therefore feel they understand what it means. However, the term itself is rather unfortunate in that it suggests a splitting of the personality. This leads many people to think of schizophrenia as an illness in which the person has a number of different personalities, which they switch between. This is in fact known as *multiple personality disorder* and is much less common than schizophrenia. The person suffering from schizophrenia, rather than having several personalities, experiences, especially in the early stages, a disintegration of their sense of themselves as a person. The splitting of the personality in the original descriptions of schizophrenia referred to the way in which the person felt they were no longer whole, as if the things which normally work together to help us understand and appreciate the world around us were not functioning properly. This process is thought to be the reason why people in the early stages of schizophrenia report feelings of confusion, increased alertness and perplexity, even before specific symptoms such as hallucinations occur.

People with multiple personality disorder do not report this degree of confusion. Each personality feels whole although it can be aware of the existence of other personalities. The types of symptoms noted above for schizophrenia are not observed in multiple personality disorder.

Are aggression and violence common in schizophrenia?

Schizophrenia has become associated in popular mythology with acts of violence and murder. In the past, people regarded those with mental illness as having unusual powers and abnormal strength when ill. This association of dangerousness and mental illness, in particular schizophrenia, has continued to this day.

There are people who have schizophrenia who have committed some terrible acts of violence. These have been widely reported in the news. This leads to a belief that all people with schizophrenia could potentially act in this way, but this does not tally with the reality of the situation. If you look at prison and hospital figures, the vast majority of people who have committed violent crimes, including murder, are not schizophrenic. In fact the most common diagnosis is usually 'normal'. It would in many ways make more sense to regard people without mental illness as potentially more dangerous than those with. The vast majority of people with schizophrenia have no history of or tendency towards violence. They have enough to deal with in gaining control over their illness and keeping up with everyday chores.

When acutely ill some people can act in an apparently bizarre manner. Someone might start to dress in a very garish way, walk very quickly or slowly, or sleep rough. Because such people are noticeable they are regarded as dangerous because their behaviour is 'not normal'. However, this is an indication of the person's vulnerability rather than their dangerousness. Such people are much more likely to meet with violence from passers by who do not understand that they are ill, than they are to inflict it themselves.

Does schizophrenic parents mean schizophrenic children?

As discussed above, schizophrenia does appear to run in families to some extent. There is evidence that vulnerability to schizophrenia is in part genetically determined. This does not mean that if you have had a schizophrenic illness your children will inevitably suffer the same illness.

In practice, if one parent is schizophrenic there is a ten to fifteen per cent chance of a child developing schizophrenia. This means that the chance of schizophrenia is higher than for the general population, but also that it is more likely (85 to 90 per cent) that the child will not develop schizophrenia. Even when both parents suffer from schizophrenia children have no more than a 50 per cent chance of becoming schizophrenic themselves.

If there is schizophrenia in the extended family, but not in parents or other first-degree relatives, risks fall well below ten per cent for children.

These figures mean that a parent with schizophrenia will not inevitably have a child with schizophrenia. Indeed if only one parent has schizophrenia it is more likely that the child will remain well. It is clearly an issue which people need to think about and discuss with their doctor, as it is a risk; but it is equally important to remember that the degree of risk is probably substantially lower than many people would think.

2
Traditional Treatments for Schizophrenia I

The present chapter will deal with a number of current treatments which will usually have been tried by some or all people with a diagnosis of schizophrenia at some time in their lives. In general most people will find that a combination of the traditional treatments outlined here and the recent advances discussed later in the book will be beneficial.

Like other human beings people with schizophrenia are all different. For some people with schizophrenia their illness is effectively controlled by taking low doses of medication provided by their GP, whereas for others with the same diagnosis the same medication will have few, if any, benefits. The same is likely to be true of other approaches; they will be of great benefit to some people, moderate benefit to others, and of little benefit to a minority. One of the tasks which people with schizophrenia, their carers and their families are faced with is deciding which combination of treatments works best for each individual person. There are no simple answers to this. Although there are people who would argue for the extreme positions of medications only, or even no medication, as being the answer for all patients the evidence is that both extremes are incorrect. For each individual the best treatment will be the one which has the greatest benefits and the fewest drawbacks. For both traditional treatments and recent advances this will involve some degree of trial and error.

Any successful treatment programme will involve a number of different elements. The elements will vary depending on the individual being treated but will almost certainly include some of the traditional approaches listed below.

Drug treatments

The development of antipsychotic drugs

It was not until the 1950s that real progress was made in the development of effective drugs for the treatment of schizophrenic symptoms. Around that time antipsychotic drugs were used for the first time. Although there had been other medication which served to sedate disturbed patients, it was not until the development of these drugs that the hallucinations and delusions experienced by people with schizophrenia could be significantly reduced. Initially the results were dramatic and reports abounded of people who had been untreatable for years responding well to this new treatment. People who had been confined to hospital and even physically restrained for decades due to the severity of their illness were able to be integrated back into general therapeutic wards.

The drugs which are used today are largely refined versions of those which first came on to the market thirty years ago. Over this time it has become clear that although such medication is an important, indeed vital, part of treatment for many people, there are others for whom its benefits are slight.

What antipsychotic drugs do

Antipsychotic medication acts to reduce the severity and frequency of hallucinations and delusions and helps people concentrate. These drugs can have calming effects, making the individual feel peaceful and at ease. This is not the main reason for their use however. Their main purpose is to reduce the severity of the symptoms of schizophrenia. People with schizophrenia will often report feeling confused and muddled; their thoughts may seem to race and they may well feel overwhelmed by all the information which their mind is trying to deal with.

Antipsychotic drugs help the brain to function in a more normal manner. The medication allows the brain to return to its more usual state of taking one piece of information at a time. The person is able to deal better with everyday situations because they are less distracted by the activity happening in their heads. The voices and other disturbances become less intrusive and in some cases disappear altogether. For those people who have voices instructing them to behave in particular ways, the voices become less convincing and easier to ignore. This is often a great relief to the person with schizophrenia who will frequently say they had no wish to act in a particular manner, but that the voices were so insistant and convincing that they felt they had no option. Other people will have successfully resisted following the instructions of voices, but found themselves under great strain as a result. With the reduction in the intrusion of such voices the associated stresses and strains are themselves reduced.

Schizophrenia is not just about hallucinations and delusions. Many people with schizophrenia feel that they have lost their drive to do things: activities which were previously engaging lose their appeal; jobs which were previously accomplished with ease become impossible to perform; even getting out of bed and performing the most basic personal hygiene can become a chore which cannot be performed. This can be a frequent source of conflict between people with schizophrenia and those who care for them and wrongly suppose they are being lazy.

Different doses for different people

As with many other aspects of treatment for schizophrenia the specific dosage and type of antipsychotic drug that will be best for each person will be different. If doses are too high the person may find that they feel more sleepy than usual during the day and continue to have trouble in performing day-to-day activities, although their other symptoms are reduced. It is the aim of the prescribing doctor to achieve a balance between improvement in symptoms and making the person feel over-tired and sleepy (which is known as over-sedation).

The names of antipsychotic drugs

- *Chlorpromazine* (trade name: largactil) is one of the most commonly used antipsychotic drugs. This is usually given in tablet form, but is also available as a liquid or as an injection. Chlorpromazine can be quite sedating, which may initially be helpful if the person is in a state of great agitation. However, for longer-term use alternative antipsychotic medication may be offered, which is less sedating.
- *Flupenthixol* (trade name: depixol) is less sedating than chlorpromazine. It is given in tablet form.
- *Haloperidol* (trade names: dozic, fortunan, haldol) is another common alternative, given in a liquid, tablet or injection form.
- *Pimozide* (trade name: orap), taken in tablet form.
- *Sulpiride* (trade names: dolmatil, sulpitil). Doses towards the higher end of the dosage range are used to control acute hallucinations and delusional experiences. Lower doses can help activate people who have become withdrawn and stopped engaging in their normal activities.
- *Thioridazine* (trade names: thioridazine, melleril) can be given in tablet form or as a liquid.
- *Trifluoperazine* (trade name: stelazine), given as tablet, liquid or injection.

Depot medication

It is fairly common for a person with schizophrenia to become well quite rapidly on a regular dose of antipsychotic medication, but then to become unwell again soon afterwards as they have begun taking their medication erratically, or not at all. This can occur for a number of reasons. It may be that the medication is addressing their psychotic symptoms, but is also causing other problems (side-effects) which are unacceptable to that person. In such a situation a discussion with the prescribing doctor should be arranged to discuss alternative types of medication which may suit the person better. Alternatively the person may feel there is no need to continue with the drugs now they are no longer troubled by their previous symptoms. However, it is unwise to withdraw rapidly from the type of medication used for schizophrenia; cautious reductions in collaboration with the doctor are both safer and more likely to lead to a permanent reduction in the long-term need for medication. Finally, it is common for the person to take the medicine erratically because they either forget or it becomes a lower priority than when first prescribed. In this situation it can be helpful to take anti-psychotic medication in depot form.

Depot medications are the same types of antipsychotics as above, given in a different form. The depot is given as an injection which the person receives periodically, between weekly and monthly. During the period between injections the medication is present at an approximately constant level and the person does not have to remember to take tablets several times each day.

Common types of depot medication

- *Flupenthixol decanoate* (trade names: depixol, depixol concentrate). This is the depot form of flupenthixol (see above).
- *Fluphenazine decanoate* (trade names: modecate, modecate concentrate).
- *Haloperidol decanoate* (trade name: haldol decanoate).

Side-effects of drug treatments

Antipsychotic medication can have a tranquillizing and even sedating effect on the person taking it. The tranquillizing action of the drug can be helpful for people who are very anxious and over-active, but will not necessarily be helpful for others. This is a side-effect of the medication which varies in degree depending on the type of antipsychotic chosen. (A side-effect is something which the drug does, which is not required for it to be clinically effective.) All drugs have side-effects to varying degrees because the science of drug development is not yet so advanced as to prevent them occurring. Some people find that they become rather stiff when on antipsychotic medication. Others experience some facial or body movements which can look quite alarming to those observing them. Restlessness may also occur. These are known as *extrapyramidal symptoms*, which can normally be stopped by simply withdrawing the drug with which the patient is being treated. However, if the drug is required to prevent a deterioration in the schizophrenia suffered by the individual then an alternative approach may be required. As with the sedating effects of some medications, the extrapyramidal symptoms caused by some antipsychotic drugs tend to be more marked than those caused by others. Unfortunately the drugs which have fewer extrapyramidal effects tend to be more sedative, and the drugs which are less sedative may have more extrapyramidal effects. It is the responsibility of the clinician, based on the reports of the client, to find the medication which is the best compromise for the individual.

An additional tool available to deal with this type of side-effect is the use of anti-parkinsonian medication. This is medication which was first developed to relieve the stiffness and trembling suffered by patients who have Parkinson's disease. It has been proven over the years that this type of medication is very helpful for the treatment of similar symptoms when they occur with antipsychotic medication. It should be emphasized that this is not to be the routine answer to extrapyramidal symptoms in schizophrenia; rather the first response should be to search for an antipsychotic which better suits that person. Only if it proves to be the case that these symptoms are otherwise unavoidable would the clinician take the step of adding a further drug to the individual treatment package.

For a more detailed discussion of anti-psychic drugs and their possible side-effects, see MIND's Special Report on Major Tranquillizers (see end of chapter for more details).

Common types of anti-parkinsonian drugs

- *Benzehexol hydrochloride* (trade names: benzhexol, artane, broflex), taken as a tablet or syrup.
- *Benzotropine mesylate* (trade name: cogentin), taken as a tablet or injection.
- *Orpehenadrine hydrochloride* (trade names: biorphen, disipal), taken as a tablet, or in liquid form.
- *Procyclidine hydrochloride* (trade names: arpicolin, kemadrin), taken as a tablet or syrup.

How long is medication needed?

If a person with schizophrenia finds that his or her condition is improved by antipsychotic medication, it is likely that this will continue to be taken for a substantial period of time. Although these drugs are generally very safe it is essential that they are taken in the manner prescribed by the doctor. It is tempting to take the medication for a while and then to stop when feeling well.

Although the desire to live without the medication is an appropriate one, there are correct and incorrect ways to find out when the time is right to do this. The correct way is to have a good working relationship with your doctor. This means keeping him/her well informed about how you are feeling and whether or not you are suffering any side-effects. It is good practice to keep a person on the minimum dose of medication which keeps him or her well. If your doctor is aware that you have been well for some time on the medication you are receiving then it may be time to think about reducing the dose taken gradually. When this is being done it is important that both doctor and client are alert for any signs of a recurrence of schizophrenic symptoms. If all goes well it may be possible to reduce the dose to a very low level or even remove it completely. However, for many people the best compromise is usually a low dose, rather than complete absence of medication.

Stopping using medication

It is known that antipsychotic drugs can help to protect the person with schizophrenia from some of the stresses of life which might otherwise cause them to become ill again. Thus, although complete withdrawal from medication is in one sense a positive step there should be an awareness that this can leave the person vulnerable to further relapse. Such risks can be minimized by finding other ways of improving resistance to stress. These are discussed in full in later chapters.

It is important that the individual who has schizophrenia becomes familiar with their own needs for medication, or lack of them. Some people find that particular times of year or particular situations are especially difficult to cope with. If you find yourself likely to be in a situation which will be stressful and will continue over some time, it would be worthwhile discussing with the doctor whether a temporary increase in medication would be appropriate to carry you over that period without risking a return to schizophrenic illness. In such circumstances it is important also to let the doctor know when the stressful situation has passed, so that return to previous levels of treatment can be arranged.

Geoff

Geoff is a 40-year-old man who worked for some years as a manager in a computer firm. He eventually left because he felt that people were conspiring against him. The main problem was that they were apparently discussing him behind his back and labelled him as homosexual. He felt that he looked abnormal and that anyone who saw him might think he was homosexual. He then began to hear voices of people discussing him and telling him that he was gay. This made him so upset and angry that he left his job and moved to a different county. Over the years he had a number of different jobs but left each one after a short period because he could not stand the voices and felt that other workers were against him. This pattern continued for some years until he finally went to see his doctor. He was diagnosed as suffering from schizophrenia and was placed on a low dose of antipsychotic medication. The voices stopped and he began to feel less convinced that other people were conspiring against him. If he was not able to express his fears to anyone for a period of time his feelings of paranoia would worsen. However, with regular opportunities to talk over his concerns and with regular low doses of medication he was able to avoid any deterioration in his condition. He did not return to his previous management job, but was able to maintain regular employment in a local government job. In this job there were still worries regarding his fellow employees, but with the opportunity to express these and the regular medication he was able to cope with them and not let them interfere with his work. From this position of greater stability in the workplace he felt able gradually to resume contact with members of his family whom he had not been in touch with since leaving his home county.

A note on ECT (electroconvulsive therapy)

When someone is given ECT they are given a course of several treatment sessions in which they receive an electric shock of sufficient voltage to ensure that they have a convulsive reaction. This sounds really rather drastic and distressing, but in fact patients are usually unaware of what is happening. They are medicated before each session so that they are relaxed and unconscious when the shock is applied. Afterwards the person comes round in a recovery room and is assessed to check that he or she is suffering no after-effects from the treatment. This procedure has in the past been used for people with schizophrenia, although it was originally developed for use in depression. There is evidence that in intractable depression patients who have remained resistant to antidepressant medication can respond, at least in the short term, to this treatment. *However, there is no substantial evidence that this form of treatment provides any benefits above standard treatment for the patient with schizophrenia*. This treatment has therefore fallen out of favour for use with this group of patients.

Managing the illness

Members of a mental health team

Most mental health teams are now called multidisciplinary teams. This means that the team consists of people from a range of different professions who work together to plan treatment for the people under their care. Such a team will vary in size and composition but will usually contain some or all of the following professions:

Nurses

Nurses are usually the most numerous members of the team. Their job is the day-to-day nursing care of patients and as such they are likely to be the most visible profession in a ward setting. There are a number of different grades of nurses reflecting their levels of training and responsibility. Nursing assistants will have gained experience on the job but have not yet enrolled on any of the available nursing courses. Staff nurses and charge nurses will have a psychiatric and often a general medical nursing qualification. Additionally some of these nurses will have taken a degree in nursing.

Nurses will be responsible for the running of the ward, for administration of medication and supervision and monitoring of patients.

Occupational therapists

Most teams will have an occupational therapist attached. She/he will be responsible for developing the occupational therapy programmes for each patient. This will usually involve an initial individual assessment in which client and occupational therapist work together to discover the client's interests and strengths, in addition to areas in which further training might be helpful. A programme is then drawn up which attempts to match the client's needs and interests with the resources available to the service. Some parts of the programme may be based in the hospital or day centre, or aspects may well be serviced by outside agencies, with the occupational therapy service performing a co-ordinating role.

Occupational therapists are trained in a two-year course.

Clinical psychologist

There is usually one psychologist associated with a team. The psychologist is clinically trained and is able to take on patients for whom they then become clinically responsible. The clinical psychologist can work psychologically with patients with the whole range of mental health difficulties. The majority of clinical psychologists offer a number of different types of help, the most common being behaviour therapy and cognitive behaviour therapy. Behaviour therapy is based on the principle that a lot of the difficulties experienced by clients result from them having learnt (for many different reasons) patterns of behaviour which are not helpful to them. In behaviour therapy, therefore, the clinical psychologist works together with the client to develop an individualized programme which will involve the client gradually reducing behaviours which are thought to be contributing to their distress and replacing them with those which are likely to make them less vulnerable to future problems. These programmes can be powerful and results over the years have been impressive. However they only work if there is a good relationship between client and therapist with both working together.

Cognitive behaviour therapy has evolved out of behaviour therapy. It is assumed in behaviour therapy that certain patterns of behaviour can serve to make people unwell or distressed; in cognitive behaviour therapy it is additionally proposed that patterns of thinking can function in a similar distressing manner. The details of cognitive work with schizophrenia are presented in a later chapter. However, cognitive therapy has been applied to the whole range of other psychiatric disorders as well as schizophrenia. In general the aim of cognitive therapy is to help the client to identify patterns of thinking which, like patterns of behaviour, cause and maintain their mental health problems. These thoughts once identified can then be challenged in a systematic manner and replaced with patterns of thinking which protect the client against further illness. This procedure can take some months with many clients as it requires a trusting therapeutic relationship for the client to take on the task of attempting to change important aspects of the ways in which they think about life, even if these have been distressing in the past.

Psychiatrist

Psychiatrists are medical doctors who have done an additional course which qualifies them to work with people who are mentally ill. There are a number of different types of psychiatrists who are likely to be present on a team. A registrar is someone who is a qualified medical doctor, who is in the process of training to become a qualified psychiatrist. Their training will normally take two to three years. They will be based on the hospital ward and are likely to have the majority of psychiatric contact with the patients. The senior registrar will have done the two years training and will be working and gaining experience prior to taking up a consultant post. The consultant will be the lead psychiatrist in the team. It used to be the case that all teams were effectively led by the psychiatrist. This is changing, more quickly in some teams than others, with many teams being run on the basis of equal representation. This means that rather than having meetings run by and for the benefit of the medical team alone, they are as likely to be chaired by members of any of the other professions as by the psychiatrist.

The psychiatrist is responsible for the prescribing of medication to the patients, although it is usually administered by nurses. They may have additional training in psychotherapeutic techniques, although this will vary. They will monitor the physical as well as mental health of the client to ensure that they are receiving the correct levels of medication.

Social workers

Social workers are responsible for helping clients with practical problems relating to housing and social security benefits. They are often involved in the development of services for clients in the community. Social workers will often also have clinical involvements with clients, including doing family therapy and other types of individual therapy and counselling.

Mental health teams in the past were mostly hospital-based. Now many teams work with people living in the community. Thus many of the assessments and interventions described will actually now take place in the client's home, at a day centre, or at an out-patient clinic.

How to get help from a mental health team

The GP is usually the first person called upon by someone who is becoming ill with schizophrenia, or by their family. If the illness does not respond to simple administration of antipsychotic medication the person is likely to be referred to a mental health professional. Some GPs have Community Psychiatric Nurses attached to their surgeries who may be asked to provide more intensive treatment. Alternatively the person may be referred to a mental health team, usually via a referral letter. They will then contact the person and assess them for their service.

Hospital

Although many people with schizophrenia now live in the community the majority will at some time or another have spent time in a psychiatric hospital. The image conjured up for many people is of a vast old victorian building, set in large grounds, probably in the country, and hidden away from the hustle and bustle of everyday life. Whilst it is true that this type of institution did exist in the past it is much less common today. These large old hospitals used to contain all services on site, so that, once an in-patient, some people never left the site for the length of their stay. Even clothes shops and food stores were contained within the hospital grounds. It is now recognized that this sort of total institution, designed for people to spend long periods of time, is not helpful for people with schizophrenia.

Psychiatric hospitals today tend to be smaller places, or even wards within general hospitals. Their role is now seen as one of last resort. People are admitted to hospital when they are at their most acutely ill and when efforts to intervene in the more normal environment have proved unsuccessful. The period of hospitalization is also now kept to a minimum. Thus whereas previously it was common for people to spend up to several years in hospital, stays now of more than a couple of months are unusual. People admitted to a psychiatric hospital should now be automatically assessed for their needs before discharge, by a responsible social worker. This is intended to reduce the likelihood of the person missing out on services which are available to help them maintain their recovery when out of hospital.

What are the purposes of hospital in the present health service? Although many people can survive very well in the community there are occasions when more intensive care may be necessary. When some people become very ill they lose the desire to take care of themselves, cease taking any medication and can be a risk to themselves or others. A common problem during a severe phase of schizophrenia is lack of awareness of danger. A person in this situation may walk up busy streets regardless of traffic or put themselves at risk of falling by climbing high objects. Under these circumstances it is often best to have a short period where the individual can be cared for intensively, which will require an admission to hospital. In this way the person is not exposed to the dangers of the outside world and is also removed from many of the potential stressors which could make their condition worse. After a short period of rest without having to deal with the day-to-day trials of life and sometimes with an adjustment to medication the person will usually be ready to return to the community.

Activity programmes

People who have nothing to do during the day become bored, restless, irritable and depressed if it goes on for too long. People who have schizophrenia are no different. Although there may be periods when their illness is too severe for them to engage in any activities, these periods will be few and far between. Just as with medication, the activity programme of any one person will have to be individualized to that person's needs and abilities.

Occupational therapy programmes

When someone is ill in hospital it is likely that activities will be less demanding than those available for people when they are living in the community. The term used for the planned activities provided by hospitals to both in-patients and out-patients is *occupational therapy*. This covers a huge range of activities from very casual unstructured groups where people may meet for a cup of tea and a chat to skilled work teams who gain contracts from industry for the goods they produce.

Occupational therapists realize the need to provide people with individualized programmes for their time in hospital and this will change as the person's condition improves. When someone is feeling very ill it may be helpful to attend a workshop to perform a very simple task for an hour every other day. However, when the same person is feeling rather better this same regimen will likely seem boring and undemanding. Flexibility and responsiveness to change are crucial ingredients in a successful programme.

Day care and what it can offer

Day care, like occupational therapy, covers a wide range of potential areas. Day care is the provision of support and some form of daytime activity to people with psychiatric problems who are not hospitalized. Some day care will be hospital-based even though attended only during the day. Unlike hospital wards, however, the staff will usually be occupational therapists rather than nurses or doctors. Day care does not have to be provided through a hospital and often is not. There are many voluntary agencies which now run day care and work schemes for people with schizophrenia and other long-term psychiatric problems.

Day centres tend to be run along quite flexible lines. Clients who attend normally do so as they wish rather than at specific times. These centres can serve as places to meet friends and to talk; they will usually have some form of medical cover which allows medication to be taken there, and they normally have some access to a counselling service if this is required.

Work programmes in day care

In addition to this, most day centres will have work programmes which clients can take part in. There are different types of work available depending on the day centre attended. Clients who are involved in the work programmes will usually be expected to give a regular commitment to the job which they take on. This does not mean that people will lose the chance to work if they happen to come in late on a couple of occasions, but if they do not attend for weeks on end then it is likely that the job, for which there is often a waiting list, will be offered to someone who is more able to benefit from it. Some of the work available is of a routine variety such as sorting or packing goods; it is relatively unskilled but does require concentration and involvement to be done properly. People who are struggling with schizophrenia will often find this to be quite an agreeable way to reintroduce themselves to the world of work; the task to be completed is normally clear and straightforward and each portion of the task can be completed in a short period of time. This type of work is helpful for people whose concentration may be affected by their illness, for instance by the periodic intrusion of hallucinations, since they can complete the job in a satisfactory manner. More advanced work is usually available for those who are ready for it. This can be provided by the day centre or by work retraining centres which provide skills courses for people who are more or less ready to return to full-time work but lack confidence or need to update their skills before they begin to apply for jobs.

Recommended leaflet on medication

Major Tranquillizers: The price of tranquility. Mind Publications, 4th Floor, 24–32 Stephenson Way, London NW1 2HD.

3
Traditional Treatments for Schizophrenia II

In this chapter we are going to take a look at more traditional treatments. However, the emphasis in this chapter is on treatments that are not drug based.

Learning about schizophrenia

Education is extremely important, not only for the individual suffering from schizophrenia but also for his or her family. A better understanding of schizophrenia often leads a patient to take a more active role in his or her self-care. Being more aware of self-help techniques reduces feelings associated with 'being helpless', and increases feelings of 'being in control'. Armed with even a rudimentary knowledge of schizophrenia, self-help strategies begin to make more sense.

Education reduces fear

The very names of some illnesses are frightening. Cancer, for example. To most people, a diagnosis of cancer means little short of a death sentence. However, medical science has made tremendous advances, even in the last ten years or so; several types of cancer can now be treated, especially if the disease is detected early. Because cancer has developed such a bad reputation as a 'killer' disease, it has been difficult to convince people that having cancer no longer means certain and imminent death.

A similar effect has occurred with schizophrenia. In the public's view, schizophrenia is equivalent to madness, for which, they assume, there is no help. We often hear reports of people 'going mad', but rarely hear about their recovery. Madness, therefore, is perceived as a permanent condition. This is particularly evident when 'madness' is depicted in fiction or films.

The situation is made worse by the ludicrous misconception that mental problems are in some way the 'fault' of those who suffer from them. This is evident in the telling phrase 'Why don't you pull yourself together!' Because mental illnesses are often perceived as the fault of the sufferer, people with schizophrenia can be made to feel ashamed of their condition, and not quite deserving of sympathy. If you have learned about schizophrenia through the press, through fiction, or through the media, then you will be presented with a frightening and confused picture.

Some of these myths and misconceptions have already been outlined in chapter 1. By learning more about schizophrenia, many of the unwarranted fears that stem from these misconceptions can be dispelled.

When a member of a family develops schizophrenia, the fear that everyone feels is largely the 'fear of the unknown'. Education will reduce that fear, by replacing misconceptions with facts.

It is far easier to cope with a problem that you understand. So, if you have schizophrenia, try to learn more about it. You can do this by talking to a health professional, or simply reading books. Most health professionals would be happy to answer any questions you have about the nature of the illness. A recommended reading list is given at the end of this chapter.

Education will help you to take care of yourself

Some people find learning about 'medical' problems difficult; after all, ordinarily, when you go to the doctor there is no need to understand the illness that you or another family member is suffering from. With many medical problems, it is quite acceptable to assume that your understanding need not go beyond knowing what pills to take and when to take them. However, schizophrenia is not like an ordinary medical problem, and understanding the nature of schizophrenia is not simply an academic exercise. It is very important that you know about the symptoms of schizophrenia, and how they can be managed. With schizophrenia, understanding the problem should not just be left to the doctors; understanding the problem will help both you and your family to cope with it.

In summary, education is important because:

- it can reduce anxiety by correcting frightening/misleading thoughts;
- it can make coping with schizophrenia easier, for both sufferer, and family. Often, just feeling more in control can be therapeutic.

You can learn more about schizophrenia by:

- talking about it to a health professional; or

- reading books or information leaflets that have been written on the subject.

Family therapy

The onset of schizophrenia can be a terrifying experience. The world may suddenly become an unpredictable and threatening place. Although schizophrenia is frightening for the sufferer, it can also be equally frightening to his or her family. A 'changed member' may be difficult to accept, or cope with. This can put a great deal of strain on existing relationships. In addition, this strain is likely to be felt most when the sufferer is having considerable problems managing symptoms or adjusting to life in the wake of a schizophrenic illness.

One of the most interesting findings to emerge recently from research into schizophrenia is that the way a family communicates can have a profound effect on the development of a family member's schizophrenic illness. To some extent, this is not new, insofar as the influence of the family has always been, to a greater or lesser extent, recognized. However, new research stresses the importance of something called *expressed emotion*, or EE. Expressed emotion research is primarily concerned with how the outcome of a schizophrenic illness can be improved, for both the sufferer and his or her family.

Expressed emotion is difficult to define; however, it usually refers to communication with emotional content. For example, a person suffering with schizophrenia might say something – perhaps unintentionally – that could be interpreted as blasphemous by a religious father. Such a father might respond with a hostile and personal statement, such as, 'You're an evil person to say that'. Alternatively, a mother might be over-involved with her daughter, and say something like, 'I've given up my job to look after you; I hope you realize that!' Such a statement might make the daughter feel very bad about herself.

Clearly, these examples are quite crude. Calling somebody 'evil' is a direct and hurtful statement, charged with emotion. However, expressed emotion can be very subtle. For example, the emotional message may not be in the words chosen by the speaker, but in the way that these quite ordinary words are said. The tone of a speaker's voice, or the expression on his or her face, can influence the meaning of seemingly harmless words.

> *David*
> David lost his job because of a schizophrenic illness that lasted six months. Being unemployed, he spent most of his time at home. His mother was a housewife. One day, David decided to do the washing-up. His mother came in while he was doing this, and said to him, 'Oh you are good'. However, her tone of voice didn't match the meaning of the words. It was said in a tone of voice that was more suited to a statement like, 'About time!' David turned around to look at his mother, who then said, 'I'm sorry . . . it is good that you're trying to help'. By apologizing, it was clear that her initial statement had been critical, rather than encouraging.

Research on expressed emotion has shown that people with schizophrenia who come from families with this kind of communication problem are more likely to relapse than those who don't. This means that an individual who recovers from a period of schizophrenic illness is more likely to have another episode if intense contact with family members is maintained.

Family therapy is usually employed to help families who show high levels of expressed emotion. This involves all the members of a household, including the patient, coming to talk to one or more therapists. Traditional family therapy usually takes place in the following way. The family sit and talk with a therapist while being watched by a team of health professionals through a one-way mirror or glass screen. This means that the team can see the family, but the family cannot see the team. The reason for this is quite simple. It is very off-putting to be watched by a large group of people. Often the team consists of a psychiatrist, a psychologist, a social worker, a nurse and an occupational therapist. Each member of the team makes a special contribution; that is why so many are needed. During a family therapy session, the therapist who is seeing the family may be guided by the team, who talk to him or her through a small electrical 'telephone' which is worn in the ear. Alternatively, the therapist may leave the family every now and again to talk to the team in person.

Although traditional family therapy is conducted in this way, not all health authorities have enough money to employ so many people at once. In which case, family therapy is conducted more informally. So, the family may see only one or two therapists, and there are no other people involved. Additionally, some people find traditional family therapy a little overwhelming, in which case alternative arrangements can usually be made.

Family therapy usually provides the whole family with an opportunity to learn more about schizophrenia. Also, family therapy provides an ideal environment in which to explore relationships. It may be the case that certain family relationships have always been poor and could be improved by the acquisition of better communication skills. Most families pick up bad habits when it comes to communicating. These habits may, over the years, become entrenched. They may be so well practised that the individuals concerned may not even be aware of them. For example, a father may be genuinely unaware that his comments are hurtful. Alternatively, a son may find himself feeling hurt, but be unable to say why. Family therapy helps to identify poor communication, and this recognition alone can be therapeutic. It also attempts to correct the bad habits acquired through years of practice.

The truly great advantage of family therapy is that it is conducted in a safe environment. Often, when families try to sort out communication problems on their own, arguments can easily develop. Resentment founded on old grudges, and conflict over things long past, can quickly rise to the surface when emotions become heated. With a family therapist present, the situation can be contained. Anger is acknowledged, but not allowed to escalate to the point where no productive discussion can take place.

Family therapy is not an admission of guilt

Before concluding this section, a few general points need to be made. During the 1960s, a number of psychiatrists and psychologists suggested that bad family relationships actually caused schizophrenia. For obvious reasons, this particular view resulted in many families experiencing terrible guilt. They felt that they were responsible for a family member's illness, and could therefore be legitimately blamed for that illness. Today the idea that families 'cause' schizophrenia has been largely rejected. As has been suggested earlier, schizophrenia is probably 'caused' by a number of factors, some of which are psychological, others of which are biological. The idea that poor communication alone within a family can cause schizophrenia is highly implausible.

If you decide to have family therapy, this is not an admission of guilt. No one will blame you for causing an 'illness'. The type of family therapy used for expressed emotion problems is concerned with improving adjustment after the illness has developed. No assumptions are made with regard to the role of family factors as a potential cause of the illness.

Although expressed emotion effects have been studied most within the home, they are by no means restricted to the domestic environment. It is possible, for example, to observe expressed emotion effects in the work environment. An individual who has recovered from a schizophrenic illness will be more at risk of relapse, if he or she has a job in a hostile or critical workplace. Expressed emotion problems are not exclusively linked with the family.

Social skills training

For people with schizophrenia, coping with social situations can be very confusing. Because schizophrenia affects perceptual processes and the ability to concentrate, the complexities of human social behaviour can easily become too demanding or too complicated to understand. It may be difficult to follow conversations or to grasp the exact meaning of certain words and expressions. In addition, people with schizophrenia have some difficulty working out the underlying 'feelings' that might account for what other people do and say. In other words, they may find it hard to read other people's emotions.

During a schizophrenic illness, the everyday world of objects and things can be confusing enough. However, the social world, which is constantly changing and full of complicated contradictory messages, can be genuinely frightening. People's behaviour is essentially unpredictable. Entering a social situation can make a person suffering from schizophrenia feel overwhelmed and out of control. For those who have recovered from a schizophrenic illness, such experiences can remain influential. They may be left feeling wary of talking to others and their self-confidence may be seriously undermined.

Social skills groups are designed to provide both support and the opportunity to practise communications skills. They usually involve getting together with others – often those who are suffering, or have suffered, from schizophrenia – in order to learn how to cope with social situations. Often the individuals in the group will set the agenda; for example, someone might want to discuss how best to cope with attending a dinner party.

First, problems are defined more specifically (e.g. 'I won't be able to think of anything to say'). Possible ways of coping are then discussed (e.g. 'Why don't you read the papers and listen to the news before you go?'). It is then usual to practise coping with the situation through role-play. This means simply acting out the situation. This can be done with the therapist or another member of the group. After role-play, people are invited to comment on how things might be improved. This kind of advice is constructive and usually given with considerable support.

Social support groups

Many people who have had a schizophrenic illness find it difficult to maintain friendships. As a result, they can get out of touch with the social world and subsequently lead relatively isolated lives. However, we all need friends and it is important to see others regularly. Social support groups are designed to help people form friendships in a safe environment. They are easy to take part in, even if you are very shy. They are usually run in hospitals, day centres or clinics, and other members of the group are usually those suffering from schizophrenia. They are informal and often do not involve therapy as such, although a therapist may be present.

General life problems are discussed, as well as things of interest. For example: 'What was on the television news last night?', 'What's in today's papers?', 'What good films are showing in the local cinema?' If you have been in hospital for a long time, then social support groups can be very worthwhile. They allow you to get back in touch with what's going on in the world, in a safe environment. They allow you to develop friendships, and to talk about your general life problems if you want to raise them for discussion. When getting started again, after a schizophrenic illness, there is a strong temptation to shy away from social situations. Although you may feel more comfortable in the short term doing this, in the long term isolating yourself is not such a good idea. After several months of isolation you may begin to feel depressed and this may trigger upsetting thoughts. Making the decision to go is often the most stressful part of it. Once you have attended a social support group a few times, and recognize a few friendly faces, going again is so much easier.

Relaxation

Often, people with schizophrenia complain about feeling tense, agitated or anxious. When this kind of restlessness develops – mostly in response to stress – thoughts are more difficult to control and the symptoms associated with schizophrenia can get worse. At such times it is useful to have a formal procedure that will help you to calm down. So far, the best method found to achieve this has been 'relaxation training'.

When psychologists talk about relaxation, they do not mean 'taking it easy', but are referring to a very specific procedure. A relaxation training programme can be broken down into three stages.

Stage 1 involves learning to relax various muscle groups which are found all over the body. This is achieved by first tensing them, and then letting the same muscles relax. The procedure is called deep muscle, or progressive muscular relaxation. When you are proficient at this, you can move on to the next stage.

Stage 2 is called 'quick relaxation'. In this stage, you are instructed to relax the same muscle groups as you did in stage 1, but without tensing them first.

Stage 3 consists of only one simple exercise. It involves getting into a relaxed state quickly by taking a deep breath, holding it for a few moments, and then exhaling slowly. As you exhale, you are advised to say the word 'relax' to yourself. This simple exercise is called 'applied relaxation' or the Rapid Relaxation Response (RRR).

Relaxation is usually taught by a clinical psychologist. If a patient finds relaxation exercises useful in a session, then he or she is usually advised to buy a relaxation tape. A list of recommended tapes is given at the end of this chapter. Psychologists often make relaxation tapes for patients if the commercial ones are considered too expensive by the patient.

Unfortunately, most people believe that relaxation 'just happens' when you are not stressed. However, this is not really the case. Relaxation is a skill and like all skills it requires practice. It is customary to practise relaxation, using a relaxation tape, for about 25 minutes every day. You start off using the deep muscle relaxation exercises described above as Stage 1. You practise these for about one or two weeks, before moving on to quick relaxation. As you get better at relaxing, you do not need to practise so much, and practice sessions can be spread further apart. Applied relaxation is used in situations that make you feel tense. It is wrong to consider applied relaxation as simply a deep breath and nothing else; it is the complete relaxation of your body within about ten seconds. This can only be achieved with considerable practice.

You can begin learning to relax right away. Although it is useful to get guidance from a psychologist, supervision is not absolutely necessary; you can make a start on your own.

Before starting, make sure that you are lying, or sitting, comfortably, with your legs and arms uncrossed. Loosen any tight-fitting clothing. Before undertaking your exercises, focus on your breathing. Don't do anything, just breathe normally. Become aware of your stomach rising – or pushing outwards – as you breathe in, and falling as you breathe out. As you breathe out, make sure that you empty all the air from your lungs; as you do so, say the word 'relax' quietly, or think it instead. Don't be concerned about breathing in, the muscles in your body will take care of that automatically. Just concentrate on your breathing for a few moments, before starting the deep muscle relaxation exercises. You should take about 25 minutes to work through the whole lot. Pause for a few moments in between each exercise. As you perform the tensing and relaxing of each muscle group, notice the difference between tension and relaxation. Become aware of how different a tense muscle feels compared to the same muscle when relaxed.

PROGRESSIVE MUSCULAR RELAXATION EXERCISES

1 *Hands*: Tense the muscles of both hands by making tight fists. Hold your fists tightly closed for about 4 seconds, then release the tension. Relax by slowly opening the fingers of both hands.
2 *Biceps*: Tense these muscles by trying to touch your shoulders with your wrists. Your arms above the elbow should feel tense. Hold the position for about 4 seconds, then return your arms to the starting position. Enjoy the feeling of relaxation.
3 *Shoulders*: Lift your shoulders up, as though shrugging. Hold for about 4 seconds, then let them drop to their usual position.
4 *Neck*: Tense by lowering your chin into your chest, but not quite touching it. Hold for about 4 seconds, then return your head to the starting position.
5 *Jaw*: Clench teeth together by closing your mouth and maintaining the pressure of the bite. Hold for about 4 seconds, then release pressure.
6 *Lips*: Press lips together. Hold together, then release.
7 *Eyes*: Screw eyes up, pressing eyelids together. Hold. Release.
8 *Forehead*: Lift eyebrows, as though enquiring. Hold for about 4 seconds, then release.
9 *Chest*: Take a deep breath in. Concentrate on your stomach

rising. Hold it for about 4 seconds, then exhale slowly. As you do so, think of the word 'relax'.

10 *Stomach*: Tense by pulling in your stomach and abdomen as much as you can. Hold for about 4 seconds, and release.
11 *Legs*: Stretch your legs out, as far as they will go. Hold the tension for about 4 seconds, then release.
12 *Feet*: Clench your feet by curling your toes. Hold the tension for about 4 seconds, then release.

These exercises are fewer than you would find on most relaxation tapes. This is because they will be easier to read and remember in this summary form. After you have mastered deep muscle relaxation, you can then try quick relaxation. In quick relaxation you do not tense muscles at all, you simply work through the same muscle groups, relaxing them. For example, you would start off by letting your attention drift to your hands. You would concentrate on the muscles, and try to let any tension ease away, leaving your hands fully relaxed. You could say the word 'relax' to yourself, as you are doing this. Then let your attention drift to the muscles in your upper arms, your biceps. Again, focus on the muscles, and try to let the tension ease away. Just continue through all twelve points described above. Focus on the muscle group, and relax.

Quick relaxation can be used to replace deep relaxation if you find it equally effective. It is less time consuming, but should still take between ten and fifteen minutes. Although replacement is recommended, there are no strict rules regarding the progress of a relaxation programme. If you find deep relaxation works better for you, then it's OK to stick with it. Practising quick relaxation is thought to be useful as preparation for applied relaxation. So working through Stages 1 and 2, before attempting Stage 3, is probably a good idea.

When you feel confident that you can reduce your tension relatively easily, try entering situations which make you feel a little tense. When you are in such a situation, employ applied relaxation to reduce your tension. Remember, you are not just taking a deep breath; you are putting into action months of practice. We have more to say about applied relaxation in the next section.

Exposure: learning to cope with fear in difficult situations

For people with schizophrenia, everyday situations can become very frightening. It might be the case that before their schizophrenic illness, they were not frightened of these situations at all. The kind of everyday situations that become frightening are often those that involve going out of the house alone, especially to places where there are crowds. Supermarkets are a typical example.

> *Lorna*
> Lorna had been in hospital for eight months. She was considerably better than on admission, and her consultant suggested that she should try going out. She agreed to do so, and left the hospital with her nurse. The hospital was situated near a high street. Lorna and her nurse went into a large shopping centre and found a supermarket in which to do some shopping. Suddenly, Lorna felt very frightened; all the people and noise made her feel confused. She remembered being in the shopping centre at the beginning of her illness, and thinking that she was being followed. As her fear rose, her thoughts began to race, and she started to look at people, wondering if she had seen them before. Her heart began to beat loudly in her ears and she began to feel short of breath. She looked at her nurse and said: 'Please, let's get out of here, I'm scared.' They left the shopping centre immediately, and it wasn't until Lorna was back inside the hospital that she felt able to talk.

For most people going to a busy supermarket can be stressful. Lorna had not been to a shopping centre for some time. If you have been in a relatively restful environment, like a hospital ward, and then you go to a supermarket, it can be experienced as intolerably hot and noisy. Lorna felt completely overwhelmed and this caused her to become frightened. Perhaps this fear prompted her to think about potential dangers, like being followed by a stranger; when frightened, unrealistic worries seem more plausible. In order to reduce her anxiety, she ran away from the situation and did not feel comfortable until she was back in the hospital.

When people feel frightened, the automatic response is usually to run away from the situation. Psychologists call this response 'avoidance'. Although avoiding or escaping feared situations reduces fear in the short term, it is probably not a good thing to do in the long term because you never get to see what would happen if you stayed in the situation.

If you ask people who are excessively frightened of everyday situations, 'What do you think would happen to you if you stayed in a situation that makes you feel frightened?', they often reply that they would 'lose control or pass out'. However, neither of these things happen. If you stay in a situation that makes you feel frightened, your fear will indeed get worse. But your fear will eventually peak and then start to decline. Most people who experience the sudden onset of fear never get to learn this because they leave the situation as soon as they experience the first signs of fear and panic.

If Lorna had stayed in the supermarket, her fear level would have continued to rise, and it might have stayed quite high for some time. However, her fear would have eventually started to go down, slowly at first.

If Lorna had returned to the supermarket, perhaps on a different day, her fear level would have risen again, but not to the level reached on the previous occasion, and not as quickly. With each attempt to stay in the supermarket, Lorna's fear would have become less and less of a problem. This is why it is so important to try to tolerate frightening situations. The more experience you have of coping with them, the easier it is to cope with them.

Encouraging people with excessive fears to enter and stay in situations that frighten them is called *exposure therapy*. For people who suffer from anxiety problems, it is usually very effective. The same level of improvement can sometimes be achieved if anxiety problems are a feature of an existing schizophrenic illness, although many exposure sessions are usually required before fears properly subside. Unfortunately, some people with schizophrenia only achieve modest improvements from exposure type treatments. Nevertheless, some improvement is better than none, and even small gains should be valued.

When you enter a frightening situation, it is difficult to say how long your fear will last before going down. This is because everybody is different. In general though, anxiety tends to rise for about fifteen to twenty minutes. When it reaches its maximum level, and you are feeling very frightened, you should expect this to last for about ten minutes. After this, there is usually a slight drop, and you will probably feel frightened for another twenty minutes or so. Anxiety then tends to drop at a slow but steady rate. An exposure session will last about an hour in total.

If you are attending a hospital or day centre and require some help with confronting feared situations, then a psychologist, nurse, or occupational therapist will probably be available to help you. Although people with anxiety problems are often asked to confront feared situations on their own, if you have a schizophrenic illness, or a history of schizophrenia, exposure sessions should be undertaken with support and you should be accompanied, at least during the first part of your programme.

Although exposure can be effective, it is necessary for the frightened person to experience at least some distress. To overcome any fear, experiencing some distress is unavoidable. However, fear can be made a little easier to tolerate if exposure is undertaken in small stages and combined with a relaxation programme. This is what happened to Lorna:

> Shortly after becoming frightened in the supermarket, Lorna spoke to the ward psychologist. He explained to her that people who had been in hospital for a long time often found it difficult to cope with the 'outside world'. He also explained how leaving certain situations when frightened would only make things worse in the long run; somehow, Lorna should try to stay in the supermarket, until her fears went away.
>
> Lorna was very worried that she would not be able to do this, but her psychologist suggested it was possible to make exposure therapy easier by coping with less stressful situations first, and also by learning to relax. Lorna then spent three weeks learning to relax; she progressed through the three stages, learning deep, quick and applied relaxation (Rapid Relaxation Response) exercises.
>
> Her psychologist then asked her to imagine that she was shopping. Just imagining being outside caused Lorna some distress. As she became tense, her psychologist instructed her to reduce her tension by using the Rapid Relaxation Response. With practice, Lorna was able to do this.
>
> The psychologist then helped her to plan something which he called a 'graded hierarchy' or 'anxiety ladder'. This involved making a list of frightening situations. Lorna's anxiety ladder is shown below. Her least fearful situation was stepping outside the ward door with a nurse. Her most feared situation was going to the supermarket alone, and waiting for her fear level to go down.
>
> The psychologist told her that she should start with Step 1 and repeat it as many times as she liked. If she felt anxious, she should do her applied relaxation exercise. He also suggested that she only try Step 2 if she was completely comfortable with Step 1. This gradual approach is called *systematic desensitization*.
>
> Lorna was able to start her programme immediately. Things went well until Step 9 (i.e. 'Walking as far as the nearest shops' without her nurse). When she tried this, she became quite frightened. Her psychologist told her not to worry, and to practise steps 7 and 8 again. Only when she felt completely comfortable doing these steps, should she attempt Step 9. After a

week, she tried Step 9 again, and found it easier to cope with. She then progressed all the way to step 12 without any more problems.

AN EXAMPLE OF AN ANXIETY LADDER

1 Just stepping outside the ward door (accompanied by a nurse).
2 Leaving the ward, and walking to the main gates (accompanied by a nurse).
3 Stepping outside the ward door on my own.
4 Leaving the hospital and walking a hundred yards down the road (accompanied).
5 Leaving the ward, and walking to the main gates (unaccompanied).
6 Walking as far as the nearest shops (accompanied).
7 Leaving the hospital and walking a hundred yards down the road (unaccompanied).
8 Walking to the supermarket (accompanied).
9 Walking as far as the nearest shops (unaccompanied).
10 Walking to the supermarket, going in, and waiting for fear to subside (accompanied).
11 Walking to the supermarket (unaccompanied).
12 Walking to the supermarket, going in, and waiting for fear to subside (unaccompanied).

If you find it difficult to cope with any situation, then try not to get into the habit of avoiding that situation. If you stay in that situation for long enough, your fear is likely to go down. The reason for this is something that psychologists call 'habituation'. This is a property of the nervous system, whereby repeated events lose their power to make you anxious. The more experience you have of a frightening situation, the less it will bother you. By constructing a graded hierarchy of feared situations, and using relaxation, you are likely to reduce the distress associated with confronting fears.

Work

Most people with schizophrenia are encouraged to do some kind of work, even when in hospital. This usually takes the form of occupational therapy. As suggested earlier, a schizophrenic illness may be temporary, or intermittent. If so, getting paid work, or pursuing a career (however modest) can be realistically considered.

There are many reasons why work is encouraged. First, being in employment, even part-time employment, is a helpful source of income. Second, being in a work environment means increased contact with people, which can help to reduce feelings of loneliness. Third, it increases self-esteem. Most people work, and if an individual with schizophrenia is able to hold down a job he or she is leading a more ordinary life. This can reduce negative feelings about being 'ill' or 'different', allowing a more definite sense of self-worth to develop.

If you are not sure whether you are up to doing a job or not, then discuss it with your doctor, nurse or therapist. There is no point pushing yourself too hard because this may put you under a considerable amount of stress. If, after evaluating your condition, it doesn't look like work is an option, don't feel bad about this. You need never be ashamed of not working, if your illness makes it too difficult for you. Among your many basic human rights, you also have a right to be ill, and have the severity of that illness acknowledged by the society in which you live.

When choosing a job, recognize your limitations. Work with them rather than against them, so that you get a job which is enjoyable and which you can do comfortably without undue stress.

Finally, if you do decide to get a job, don't forget to take all your holidays. If you work all the time, then you are likely to get bored with the job or begin to experience persistent tiredness. By having sensible breaks, you will be refreshed and in a better position to maintain your interest in work.

Recommended relaxation tapes

'Relax and Enjoy It', by Robert Sharpe. Available from Aleph One Ltd, The Old Courthouse, High Street, Bottisham, Cambridge CB5 9BA.

'Self Help Relaxation', by Jane Madder. Available from Relaxation for Living Ltd, 29 Burwood Park Road, Walton on Thames, Surrey KT12 5LH.

Systematic Relaxation Pack, by Roy Bailey. Available from Winslow Press Ltd, 9 London Lane, London E8 3PR.

Recommended books about schizophrenia

J. J. Jeffries, M. V. Seeman, E. Plummer, J. F. Thornton, *Living and working with schizophrenia*, Oxford University Press 1990.

L. Kuipers and P. Bebbington, *Living with mental illness: A book for relatives and friends*, MHF: Human Horizons Series 1987.

4
Recent Advances

In the last two chapters we have talked about a number of different treatments which have proved helpful to people with schizophrenia over the years. Most people with a schizophrenic illness will be familiar with some or all of them. In this chapter we will outline a range of newer treatment techniques which are less traditional and therefore probably less familiar. We would like to stress that because these techniques are so new they have not been as fully developed as those described earlier. This means that we know they are beneficial for some people with schizophrenic illness, but it is not yet known whether they will be helpful for everyone who has schizophrenia. For example, cognitive therapy is only useful for those people who find that the unusual beliefs and experiences related to their illness are distressing and are able to take an active role in therapy.

A good approach to this chapter would be an experimental one. Being experimental means being flexible. In this case it involves trying a particular technique which appeals and then seeing if it works for you. If it does work then continue to use it; if it doesn't then you need not continue with it. Another of the approaches in this chapter may be more helpful. As always, you may find it helpful to discuss some of these techniques with a health professional; a clinicial psychologist would be particularly helpful with respect to the ideas outlined in this chapter.

Most of these techniques tend to be increasingly effective once the person is used to using them regularly. So, providing a particular technique doesn't make you feel worse – which would be extremely unusual – continue to practise it, expecting slow but consistent progress for at least a number of weeks. If you find that there is no improvement after this time then it would be appropriate to reconsider whether or not you want to continue.

One of the advantages of working with a health professional is that they are likely to notice small but significant changes which might escape your attention. If you have been ill for a long time, small changes are difficult to identify and may even be dismissed. This could lead you to abandon an effective approach too early before giving it a fair chance to work.

Cognitive therapy

Cognitive therapy has been used as a treatment for depression and anxiety for the last twenty years, and has proved to be effective for a large number of people. In the last few years it has been adapted for use by people with schizophrenic illness where it is clear that it has benefits for at least some people with that illness.

At its most simple, cognitive therapy involves learning to change the way we think about particular situations. This is done by learning to question unhelpful thoughts, previously assumed to be true, and then replacing them with more helpful thoughts. Cognitive therapy usually involves a number of stages.

Stage 1

In Stage 1 the patient has an opportunity to get to know the therapist and to talk in general terms about his or her problems. It is important that a trusting relationship develops between client and therapist so that the client feels comfortable talking about their unusual experiences and beliefs. It is often the case that people with schizophrenia become reluctant to talk about their symptoms because when they have done so in the past people have reacted badly. During cognitive therapy it is important that the patient is able to discuss any unusual experiences or beliefs without fear of embarrassment. This may take some time and indeed it is unusual for people to talk about these issues in great detail in the first couple of sessions.

During this stage the client and therapist will also look at the person's general lifestyle, to see if there are any features of this which may be making their problems worse. The sorts of things which would be addressed in this way are covered in chapters 5, 6, and 7; for example, stress, anxiety and day-to-day living problems and how to cope with them.

Stage 2

In Stage 2 the client and therapist concentrate on describing the development of the person's symptoms. The therapist is interested in exploring events and feelings before, after and during the first onset of the illness. Another important issue would be understanding what factors influence whether the illness gets better or worse at different times.

Many people with schizophrenia feel that their experiences and beliefs came upon them out of the blue. However, a thorough assessment will usually reveal significant events or changes in the person's life around the time that these experiences and beliefs first occurred.

The symptom history which is taken in Stage 2 will form the basis of many of the more specific approaches which are discussed later. In addition, there are basically two main aims for the client at this stage:

- To recognize that there was a time when they did not have odd beliefs and experiences. Even an initial acknowledgement by the client that they have already experienced a change in their way of thinking can be a useful starting point for further therapeutic work.
- To recognize that thoughts and experiences may be triggered, or made worse, by readily identifiable events or situations.

Stage 3

In this stage one attempts to change thinking directly by a discipline of self-questioning. Most people with schizophrenia have several beliefs which they hold with varying degrees of conviction. In cognitive therapy the therapist will ask the client to make a list of beliefs ranging from those that are very strongly held to those about which they may have some doubts. These beliefs can relate closely to unusual experiences and/or to the world in general.

Once a list has been developed the therapist will prompt the client to question the least held belief. This is usually achieved by the therapist simply asking the client what evidence they have to support their belief. The value of this evidence might then be tested through discussion. Alternatively, the therapist might urge the client to test his or her belief by conducting a small experiment. For example, if a client believes that people are always watching him or her, the therapist might accompany the client in a relevant situation. It is usually possible in such circumstances for the therapist to demonstrate that the belief is not entirely true, although it may require this demonstration in a number of situations before the client feels ready to challenge the belief.

Similar principles may be used with beliefs which are more firmly held once the client has become accustomed to the process of challenging beliefs about which they already have some doubts. We would like to stress that changing the way you think is not easy for anyone, whether they have a mental health problem or not. If you are used to thinking in a certain way then it is likely that you do so automatically. Like all habits, your unhelpful thinking will be difficult to change. Therefore it is necessary to gain considerable practice at challenging unhelpful thoughts. What you learn with your therapist must be practised as much as possible outside sessions. In fact, most therapists give their clients homework assignments to do in between sessions. Undoubtedly your therapist will be aware of the difficulty of challenging long-held and unhelpful beliefs and will not expect you to be able to change them overnight.

Stage 4

This begins when the client has made gains which he or she wants to maintain or preseve. For some people this will mean that they have successfully challenged and modified all their unhelpful beliefs; for others this process will not be fully completed.

Even beliefs which have been successfully challenged during treatment may recur in some form during periods of stress or anxiety. If this does happen it does not mean that previous therapy sessions have been wasted. On the contrary, the challenging skills that you have acquired can be practised again in order to modify upsetting thoughts.

Usually cognitive therapists like to keep in touch with their clients even after the intensive phase of therapy has been completed. This normally involves the client attending the therapist's clinic on an occasional basis (monthly or less), with attendance eventually being reduced to as little as one visit every three or six months. The purpose of these sessions will be to monitor progress and to discuss the application of techniques already learnt.

The above provides an overview of a cognitive therapy programme. Please note that cognitive therapists have different ways of working and the person whom you choose to see may not follow the stages exactly as described. However, he or she is very likely to follow a similar set of stages and will almost certainly urge you to challenge unhelpful beliefs and ideas.

Ways to improve concentration

Many people with schizophrenic symptoms find it very difficult to concentrate. This makes not only day-to-day living very difficult but also impairs the individual's ability to follow through trains of thought. People who have schizophrenia, however, have found that by planning ahead they have been able to compensate for these problems. Planning ahead means trying to structure your time as far as possible so that unexpected stresses and distractions are minimized. Most people find that planning is best achieved by using a kind of diary. Obviously it is difficult to plan for things too far in the future. However, it is practical to have a good idea of what one is doing up to a week in advance. It is also very difficult to plan when you feel stressed, so that plans are usually best drawn up during a quiet period in the day when you are feeling relaxed.

When undertaking any task always recognize your limitations. If you have a problem with concentration and are about to tackle a task that will take some time be sure to plan for rest periods. Many people with schizophrenia tire easily and it is essential to take this into account when undertaking any task requiring concentration and effort. It is always better to finish an assignment slowly than to overtire yourself so that it becomes impossible to complete.

Using an ear plug

Auditory hallucinations, such as hearing voices, can of course be very distressing. One novel way of dealing with this distressing experience is by using ear plugs. Some people with schizophrenia have found that by placing an ear plug in the left ear, auditory hallucinations have been reduced. In some cases, illusory sounds disappear altogether, although in most cases the effects are less dramatic. This technique is again best employed together with the help of a therapist.

Usually a psychologist would give you a number of hearing tests before starting this kind of therapy. These are to establish which is your 'strongest' ear – usually the right ear. When an ear plug is used, it is best placed in the 'weaker' ear.

There are a number of ideas as to why this technique works, but at present nobody really knows the specific reasons for its success with some people with schizophrenia.

Using a personal stereo system

The personal stereo system, or Walkman, is a piece of equipment that many people with schizophrenia have used spontaneously, to help them cope with their symptoms. Psychologists have begun to encourage the systematic use of personal stereos among people who may not have thought of it as a therapeutic tool. In general, people use the personal stereo system for two main reasons: distraction and to cover up distressing voices.

With regard to distraction, people often find that distressing thoughts or voices become less intrusive when they are listening to something which they find interesting and involving. The personal stereo can therefore be used to play favourite music or radio programmes. By listening to these, they become less involved with what is going on in their heads, and more involved with enjoying the music or programme.

Covering up is sometimes also called 'masking'. Some people report that certain passages of music, when played at sufficient volume, are able to 'cover up' their auditory hallucinations. This lasts for as long as the music is played. If you find this technique helpful, then please recognize that listening to loud music for too long can damage your hearing. Try to limit the use of this technique to those times when you really need it, when voices or distressing sounds are most severe.

Liz

Liz, a 22-year-old woman, had a five-year history of schizophrenic illness. This illness had resulted in several periods of hospitalization. Her most distressing symptoms were auditory hallucinations. When she was feeling particularly bad, she would hear voices. These voices would be insulting, and accuse her of being a bad person. Occasionally she would hear a man shouting that her family 'hated her', and would eventually try to 'kill her'. Sometimes there were several voices, all vying for her attention, shouting and screaming. At such times, these voices would make life unbearable; it was impossible to think straight, and Liz would become very depressed. Twice in her life, these voices had got so bad she attempted suicide. Fortunately, both attempts had been unsuccessful. Although the voices were more or less present, all of the time, they were only really bad for periods of up to two hours. After this, the voices usually subsided to their usual level. Although Liz recognized that these voices were not real, and that the things they said were untrue, the voices still caused her considerable distress. Liz found her medication helpful, but it did not really have much effect on the voices.

Liz enjoyed music – classical music rather than pop. She would listen to orchestral pieces on her Walkman when she felt tense. As a result of listening to the music, she found it easier to relax. One day, she was feeling particularly depressed and her voices were very loud. In order to relax she played one of her favourite pieces of music: Beethoven's *Ninth Symphony*. This is a piece that starts with an orchestra, but later on a choir joins in. Liz noticed that during the first part of the piece, her voices were still troubling her. However, when the choir joined in, it was as though the choir was able to block out the voices. When she turned the volume up the unpleasant voices were no longer noticable.

When Liz talked to her psychologist about this, he suggested that they do an experiment. She should try out different pieces of music, to see which one worked best at covering up the voices. They selected several. It soon became apparent that choral music was better than orchestral music alone, or a combination of orchestra and choir. They also found out that loud, happy-sounding music worked better than soft, sad-sounding music. Eventually, Liz was able to identify a piece by Bach that worked best.

Most of the time, Liz tolerated her voices and was able to cope. However, when the voices got particularly bad (and she began to feel depressed), she would play her Bach cassette. This had the effect of blocking out the unpleasant shouts and screams. Because bad periods never lasted for more than two hours, Liz was able to use the music to see her through critical periods, in which she would otherwise have been extremely vulnerable.

Living with unusual experiences

Professionals are becoming increasingly aware that there are a substantial number of people who have odd beliefs and experiences but appear to suffer no ill effects. This is to say, they have no contact with mental health services and otherwise live an apparently normal life. For some people with schizophrenia, their problem may lie more in their distressed reaction to unusual experiences, than in the unusual experiences themselves.

This means that one should develop an accepting attitude. Some of the techniques employed during cognitive therapy are helpful in developing the confidence required to accept the occurrence of occasional unusual experiences. One should try not to react to unusual experiences, and, perhaps more importantly, try not to worry about reacting. Many people who experience hallucinations, for example, report grave concerns about reacting to them in a public place, when in fact they rarely, if ever, have done so. A useful thing to do when experiencing hallucinations is relaxation (see chapter 3). It will be beneficial for two reasons: it will make you feel less anxious in a situation that would otherwise cause you to feel anxious; the relaxation exercises will provide you with some distraction. The combination of distraction and reduced anxiety make accepting unusual experiences considerably easier.

5

Managing Stress, Anxiety and Anger

In the next few chapters we are going to consider a number of problems that are relevant to people suffering from schizophrenia. These include anxiety, coping with anger, practical problems, sleep difficulties and forming intimate relationships.

Managing stress and anxiety

It is widely recognized that stress and anxiety can cause serious problems for people with schizophrenia. Treating anxiety while an individual is in the middle of a schizophrenic illness is rather difficult. It is often necessary to wait for the more serious symptoms to subside before any meaningful work is possible. If you have had a schizophrenic episode, it does not mean that you will inevitably have another one, but you are more at risk than someone who has never had a schizophrenic episode at all. Therefore, managing your anxiety and stress levels is an important part of what is often termed 'relapse prevention'.

Stressful situations are of many types. Nevertheless, we can put them into two categories: major life events and daily hassles. A major life event is something like a death in the family, or losing a job. Major life events are largely unavoidable, and have a dramatic impact on the way we lead our lives. Daily hassles, on the other hand, are things like receiving a large bill or having a domestic argument. Although these events do not have a profound effect on our lives, they are still worthy of attention. If you cxperience too many hassles, for too long, then you will probably begin to feel anxious and worried all the time. Unlike major life events, daily hassles are easier to avoid, and we will be considering them in greater detail later on in this chapter.

Although stress and anxiety are very closely related, a distinction can be made. Stress generally refers to stressful situations. When an individual becomes 'stressed', the demands of the situation exceed his or her ability to cope with it. When this happens, the person may feel anxious and experience worry.

Sadly, there isn't very much you can do to avoid the kind of major life events that cause severe distress. Most people can expect to experience one or two significant upheavals during the course of their lives. Although you cannot stop some bad things happening, you can at least make sure there are people around who could support you if the need arose. These could be health workers or friends. One of the reasons why it is so important to keep in touch with services provided by the NHS, is that you should then have access to people who know you well and whom you can talk to if something untoward does happen in your life. Most people, whether they have psychological problems or not, need to talk about distressing events in order to come to terms with them.

When individuals with schizophrenia experience stress, anxiety and worry are likely to follow. It is often the case that people who have come through a schizophrenic illness report that the early warning signs included anxiety and worry, which were probably related to stressful events in their lives at the time. The relationship between stress, anxiety, and schizophrenic illness can be represented using a simple diagram:

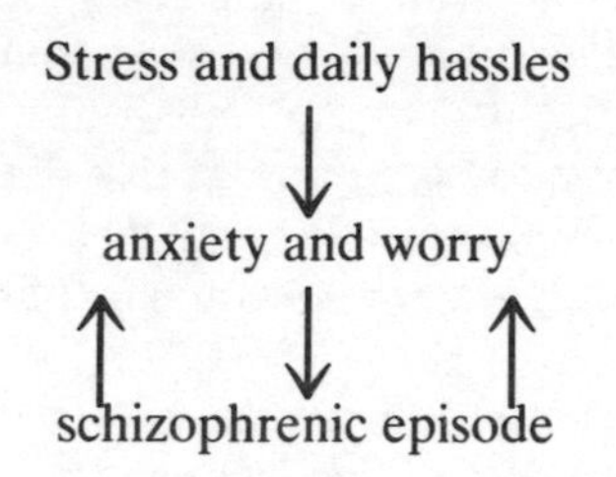

The suggestion here is not that stress causes schizophrenia; rather, if you are vulnerable to schizophrenia, then too much stress will make the illness more likely to develop and its development will be accelerated.

An important implication of the above diagram is that if you reduce the number of stressful events in a person's life, then you might also reduce the chances of that person relapsing. However, life is a stressful business and it is virtually impossible to lead a totally stress-free life. In fact, it is extremely unlikely that you will be able to go through a single day without experiencing some hassle or other. The important thing is how you respond to these hassles; if you respond to a hassle by becoming anxious and worried, you will be less able to cope. Therefore, managing your anxiety is extremely important.

What is anxiety?

Anxiety is the name we give to an unpleasant emotional state, usually experienced when we feel threatened. If we look at anxiety more closely, we can break it up into three components. First, physical changes. When people are anxious, their bodies feel different; they experience symptoms such as increased heart rate, butterflies in the stomach, muscle tension and breathlessness. There are many others, but these are the most common. Second, when people are anxious they experience anxious thoughts. These can be in the form of single sentences; for example, 'I'm going to fail my exam', or a whole series of sentences strung together, as in worry: 'What if I fail my exam, then I won't be able to get a job . . . and then I won't earn any money . . . and that will be terrible.' Finally, when you are anxious, you behave differently. For example, you might start trying to avoid situations that make you feel anxious. For our purposes, it is important to consider the first two components: physical changes and thoughts.

These two components tend to create a vicious circle: when you have anxious thoughts, you tend to get tense; when you get tense, you become more aware of your anxious thoughts. This vicious circle makes it difficult to stop worrying.

The vicious circle in anxiety

Breaking out of the vicious circle

In order to stop things getting worse, it is necessary to break out of the vicious circle of anxiety. If you don't break the vicious circle, then your anxiety can escalate, making it very difficult to deal with day-to-day problems. When this happens, you might feel that things are getting out of control, making your anxiety worse still. The end result of this can be intense feelings of distress and very serious concerns about getting ill again.

So, how can you break this vicious circle? We have already mentioned one of the easiest methods in chapter 4 – relaxation. If you calm down, your thoughts become easier to control. When you use a formal relaxation procedure, you are relaxing various muscle groups. This is helpful in itself, because you are reducing tension. However, it is probably also effective because you are distracting yourself from your worries. Once you are able to think straight, then it is possible to work out ways of dealing with the problem that caused you distress in the first place.

When we discussed relaxation in chapter 4, we recommended relaxation tapes. Using a relaxation tape is helpful because the voice on the tape will instruct you to perform the exercises at an appropriate pace. If you find while doing your relaxation exercises that thoughts are still disturbing you, then try not to get involved with them. Let them come into your mind, but don't 'think about them'. Sometimes using images helps. Imagine that they are like clouds passing overhead on a windy day; let them come and go. Another way of dealing with distracting thoughts is simply to count them. Don't consider their meaning, just give them a number and carry on concentrating on your relaxation exercises.

Remember that relaxation is a skill; it needs to be practised if you want to be good at it. So don't wait for something bad to happen before you get out your relaxation tape. Try to listen to it at least once a week. This will enable you to develop the skill of relaxation, so that when you really need to relax you can do so with minimal effort.

Another important point to remember is that, because anxiety tends to gain momentum, the earlier you notice it, the easier it is to stop it. Be aware of early warning signs; if you feel a little tense, then immediately try to relax. Don't wait until your anxiety has started to get out of control.

Lenny

Lenny had always wanted to do well at school. When he was 15, he was taking his O levels, and was under a considerable amount of stress, much of it due to the very high standards he set for himself. Although he was doing quite well, he began to think that he was going to fail. His worries about failure got worse and worse, and he started to imagine that the world was against him. He even began to think that his family were going to poison him. He became so distressed that he had to be admitted into his local hospital.

After some months he was discharged, and everything was OK

for some time. He got his O levels and went on to take A levels. In his first year at college, he began to worry about failing again. He did not talk to anybody about his concerns, but started to study very hard. He would come home from college, shut himself up in his room and work until he fell asleep. He had very little time for friends and became quite isolated. Although his family suggested he work less and go out more, his fear of failure made him work harder still. Very soon his worries began to take on the same disturbing quality as they had when he was at school. He began to think that he was a bad person, that he should be punished, and that his family might rightfully poison him. He became extremely agitated, and once again had to be admitted into hospital.

As a result of his second hospital admission, Lenny was unable to finish his first year at college. However, he decided that he would go back to college the following September and start the first year again. This time he asked his doctor if he could see a clinical psychologist, who saw him every two or three weeks at the hospital, in order to discuss stress management. Relaxation training was part of the treatment.

Everything went well until November, when Lenny was given a number of assignments which he found difficult to finish. He started to get behind with his work; he became anxious about failure, and convinced that he was going to become ill again. He started to think, 'It happened like this before . . . it's going to happen again.' This thought made him more anxious still. His worry made him more tense and his tension made him more aware of his worries. Very soon his thoughts seemed completely out of control. It became impossible for him to concentrate on his work and this seemed to confirm his worse fears; he was definitely becoming ill again; his body felt strange and he could not stop his racing thoughts.

By chance, he happened to have an appointment with his psychologist. As soon as Lenny arrived, his psychologist realized that something was very wrong. Lenny was agitated, nervous and could not keep still. He was so agitated he could only just about explain what had happened.

The psychologist asked Lenny to lie down and talked him through his relaxation exercises. Although it was difficult for Lenny, he was eventually able to calm down, and after about forty minutes he was feeling much better. His heart had stopped racing, his thoughts seemed less out of control. The psychologist then described calming scenes to him: for example, watching a sunset while sitting on a beach. Lenny imagined all the things his psychologist was describing, which calmed him even further. With every wave he imagined breaking on the seashore, his depth of relaxation increased. He had managed to break out of the vicious circle of anxiety; he was feeling exhausted, but relieved.

More about worry

Worry often occurs in response to stressful events. More often than not, these take the form of everyday hassles. If you ask people what they worry about, then worries can be grouped under several headings. These include:

- Worries about relationships; in particular, getting on with partners, friends and family.
- Worries about coping with social situations and lacking confidence in them.
- Worries about having no direction in life and not achieving ambitions.
- Worries about not having enough money and getting into debt.
- Worries about work; that is, not being able to cope with the demands of a job or study.

If you go over a problem again and again in your mind, it is very easy to get it completely out of proportion; it's as though you are 'blowing it up'. For most people, worry leads to more worry. But worry can be useful. If you don't let it get out of hand, you can use worry like an alarm; it tells you that something is wrong in your life and that you should do something about it. Instead of worrying more, just stop, and listen to what your worry is telling you. You can then try to do something about the problem.

Problems are best addressed in a systematic way. If you have a systematic plan, then problems are less likely to make you feel overwhelmed. The plan for problem-solving involves a number of simple stages.

A step-by-step guide to solving problems

1 Define the problem. Try to establish specifically what it is that you are worrying about.

2 Think of things that you can do to solve the problem. It doesn't matter if your initial ideas aren't very impressive; just try to think

of as many ideas for solving your problem as you can. Perhaps you could write your ideas down on a piece of paper.

3 Try to work out which solution is best. This stage is a bit tricky insofar as you have to evaluate which of your ideas is the most likely to succeed. A good way of doing this is to list the costs and benefits associated with each. The solution that has the least costs, and the most benefits, is the one you should choose. It might be worth talking about costs and benefits with a friend, health professional or member of your family before you make a final decision.

4 Finally, try to put your solution into action as soon as possible. Remember, the longer you leave a problem unresolved, the longer you'll be worrying about it.

Let's now go back to our example of Lenny, to see what happened in the rest of his session with the psychologist.

More about Lenny

Once Lenny had calmed down, he was then in a much better position to deal with his problem. He recognized that he had entered a vicious circle of worry and tension, each making the other worse. He also saw how he had jumped to the conclusion that he was going to get ill again. This frightening thought had made him feel worse, seemingly confirming his fear.

His psychologist explained to him that he was in fact 'winding himself up', that the problem was, in itself, not so bad. After all, many people get behind with their work when they are studying. The real problem here was Lenny's response to being under stress. If Lenny had stopped and thought about his situation, he might then have been able to work out an appropriate solution. Instead, he had let his worry lead to more worry.

Once Lenny had acknowledged what was going on, he then set about defining the problem: he had two assignments that needed to be completed by the following week. His psychologist asked him to think up some solutions. Lenny came up with several, the most realistic of which were these: first, to work really hard; second, to talk to his tutor at college and ask for more time. The benefit of the first solution was that he could get both assignments handed in before the deadline. However, there were several costs, the main one being that he would put himself under considerable stress again. He recognized that this might result in him not being able to cope at all. The second solution was beneficial, insofar as the pressure would be off. However it was also costly because he felt that he was letting himself down. His psychologist then asked him whether other students at college requested more time in which to complete their assignments. Lenny said that many did so.

They then talked about how Lenny was perhaps expecting too much from himself. After all, it wasn't so long ago that he was in hospital. Lenny accepted this, and agreed that he should ask for a few more weeks in which to complete his work. If he insisted on pushing himself, he might not be able to cope with the stress at all. Clearly this cost would be a great one.

The following day Lenny implemented his solution and went straight to his tutor. His tutor said that he could have the extra time and assured him that others too had had problems with this particular piece of work. When Lenny saw his psychologist for the next session, he was doing fine. After dealing with his problem, he felt less stressed and was able to work faster than before.

How not to cope with stress

Sometimes, when problems get out of hand, it is tempting to just 'get out of it'. Some people with schizophrenia choose to achieve this by drinking too much or by using illegal drugs. The most commonly used illegal drug is cannabis or marijuana (sometimes also called 'pot', 'grass', 'weed', or 'ganga'). It is usually taken in the form of a roll-up cigarette called a 'joint'. Although it may make you feel more relaxed in the short term, it will be of no help in the long term. There is evidence to suggest that cannabis can make the symptoms of schizophrenia considerably worse in some individuals. It may also provoke a relapse. Finally, possession of this drug is illegal and may result in prosecution and/or imprisonment.

Alcohol is also unhelpful. Getting drunk will only offer temporary escape from day-to-day problems. When the alcohol stops working, all your problems will still be there. In addition, alcohol, like cannabis, has been known to make some of the symptoms of schizophrenia worse. Finally, many fights happen when people are drunk because too much alcohol makes it very difficult to control anger. This brings us to our next topic.

Stress and anger

When under stress, many people with schizophrenia report feeling frustrated and angry. Further, this anger often leads to unnecessary arguments and conflict. At worse, conflict situations can escalate to the point where violence occurs. Trouble with neighbours, provocation, or simply not being able to cope, can all be very distressing. When someone is upset, anger can easily find expression in a violent act.

We should start off by saying that there is nothing wrong with being angry. Like worry, anger has a function. When we feel anger, we know that something is wrong; we feel motivated to do something about it, and often experience an accompanying energy surge. Feeling 'worked up' makes it easier for us to do things which would normally require a lot of effort. Finally, anger lets people know exactly how you are feeling. An angry expression often says more than many words could ever say.

Anger is only a problem if it is too easily triggered, or is excessive. If you become very angry, when such anger is not really appropriate, then you are not doing yourself any good. Nobody likes to feel angry; after all, it isn't a very pleasant emotion. Although it can be useful, few people feel good about themselves after an angry outburst. Anger tends to disrupt thinking, which is something to be avoided if you are vulnerable to schizophrenic illness. When angry, it is easier to lose control and hit somebody. Finally, if you lose your temper too often it is easy to acquire a reputation. A bad reputation means fewer friends, less support, and in all likelihood more unhappiness. If, on the whole, you feel that your anger is appropriate, then the next section doesn't apply to you. If, however, you feel that you have a tendency to become angry, even over trivial matters, then it is probably worth giving the next section careful consideration.

What makes you angry?

In general people don't become angry over nothing. People can become angry for a variety of reasons.

- They might become angry in certain situations.
- They might become angry because of the way they think and feel in response to certain situations.
- They might become angry because they don't handle certain situations appropriately.

We shall consider each of these points in greater detail.

Situations

When thinking about becoming angry, it is worth considering if certain situations make you feel more angry than others. It is very useful to think about situations that trigger anger, because if you're feeling particularly upset, or fragile, you can then make a point of avoiding them. Here are some situations that are commonly associated with anger.

Frustrating situations. Frustrating situations are those in which others prevent you from doing something that you want to do. Or situations in which a request you make isn't granted.

Abusive situations. Abusive situations are those in which you are either called names or taunted. At worst, an abusive situation might involve physical abuse; for example, being pushed, shoved or punched.

Unfair situations. Unfair situations are those in which you feel that you have suffered some kind of injustice. For example, being the victim of prejudice, or being at a disadvantage because someone made a snap-judgement about you or your circumstances.

To these we can add general irritations. Even small ones can build up over time; noise and being interrupted are typical examples.

Thoughts and feelings

Earlier, we suggested that anger could arise because of the way we think and feel in certain situations. The 'meaning' that we give situations is particularly important. If we take things too personally, this will clearly upset us. Similarly, the kind of expectation we have can determine whether we become angry or not. Often, anger arises when our expectations of ourselves and others are too high. Such high expectations can easily lead to disappointment and frustration. However, probably the most important factor is what you actually say to yourself at the time. If you are in a difficult situation and you are saying to yourself, 'That's it! That's really it! I've had enough! I've really had it now!', then such thoughts can only increase feelings of anger.

When discussing anxiety, you will remember that we made much of the vicious circle of anxiety; that is, the way thoughts and physical tension make each other worse. Exactly the same things happens with anger. If you're thinking angry thoughts, you will become more tense, and if you become more tense, then it will be more difficult to think straight. Together, thoughts and tension can create a vicious circle leading to a loss of control.

People often become angry when they have been under stress. This is probably because the tension has been building up for some time. All it takes then is an angry thought to set the vicious circle turning, and suddenly tempers are frayed and angry words spoken. In general, people who lead more stressful lives tend to have 'shorter fuses'.

A final thing to consider in this section on thoughts and feelings is ill-humour. If you are feeling grumpy, upset or miserable, you are likely to be more easily provoked.

Handling difficult situations

Another important factor that determines whether or not you become angry is what you actually do in difficult situations. For example, during the course of a domestic argument it is sometimes unhelpful to walk away without resolving the problem. It is likely that you will continue to think about the situation, and anger might soon turn into feelings of resentment. Sometimes, failing to resolve a situation can result in a loss of self-esteem. You can easily feel that you have let yourself down and subsequently feel depressed or useless.

Totally withdrawing from conflict situations is clearly unhelpful. However, so is the exact opposite. Becoming too involved in an argument, antagonizing and provoking can result in hostility and aggression from others. So it would seem the best thing to do is to occupy some sort of middle ground. It is important to be aware of how you are feeling in the situation. If you begin to feel overwhelmed by it, be prepared to remove yourself from the situation until you feel better able to cope with it.

In summary, we have said that certain situations might reliably trigger angry feelings. Further, such anger can be useful. However, if your anger escalates, then it is possible to lose control of yourself and the situation. Whether or not you lose control will depend on what you think, what you feel, and what you do.

Some hints for controlling anger

First of all, remember that anger is an emotion with a message. It lets you know that it's time to take some form of constructive action. Second, being in an angry state means that you will have sufficient energy to accomplish whatever is necessary. When we talk of controlling or managing anger, we are talking about a set of simple strategies that will enable you to stay in command. Things only go wrong when anger takes command of you! Anger management means taking immediate action in order to overcome a problem. To do this, you have to keep your mind on the job and not be distracted.

Managing your thoughts

Here are a few words about self-understanding. Always try to understand how your feelings come about. If you have some insight into why you become angry, then you are a good way towards being able to do something about controlling your anger. Questions about *why* a person becomes angry are very different from those questions about *what* makes a person angry. The latter can be answered with relative ease. However, the former question, the 'why' question, is not so easily answered. In addition, the answers given to 'why' questions are usually more complicated. The reasons why we behave in one way rather than another can be influenced, for example, by previous experiences and previous relationships.

Joanna

Joanna was attending a day centre. One of the people at the day centre, a man called Ron, really annoyed her. It seemed to her that whenever she had anything to do with him at all, she became very angry. One day she was playing a board game with him. After she moved her piece, Ron said, 'That was very silly . . . very silly indeed.' Joanna felt a surge of anger and without thinking upset the board, scattering the pieces all over the floor.

Later that day, one of the counsellors at the centre asked Joanna if she would talk to her about what had happened. The counsellor asked Joanna why she always became angry when she was with Ron. At first Joanna found it was impossible to say why. However, with time, it became apparent that she perceived Ron as always being critical of her. Further, she said that Ron reminded her of her father; he, too, had always been critical.

The sort of critical comments Ron made, although irritating, were not really that offensive. Coming from anybody else, Joanna would not have become angry. The fact that Ron reminded Joanna of her father was the crucial factor. When Ron criticized her, the anger she felt was somehow more intense.

After talking to the counsellor, Joanna realized why she was becoming angry without good reason. She was, to some extent, confusing Ron with her father. The anger she felt towards Ron was largely left-over anger that had been provoked at home.

Once she realized what she was doing, Joanna found it easier to cope with Ron's manner.

Understanding others

In addition to self-understanding, it is also important to understand the thoughts and feelings of others, especially the people you are angry with. It is possible that you are misunderstanding their intentions; or, alternatively, they are having difficulty communicating their intentions, and things are coming out wrong. Trying to understand how others are feeling in a difficult situation can be very helpful in controlling your anger. If you can see things from their point of view, it is easier to reach a compromise. Let's see what happened next with Joanna.

More about Joanna

The counsellor at the day centre also talked to Ron. As it happens, Ron didn't think he was being critical of Joanna at all. He thought that he was being kind and helpful. In fact, he liked Joanna very much and was only aware of 'putting her right' when he thought she was about to make a mistake. He had only called her 'silly' when playing the board game in order to stop her from making a move that would have lost her the game.

When Joanna heard this, she found that her feelings towards Ron changed even more. She said that she was sorry for reacting in the way she did. However, the counsellor suggested to Ron that he stop trying to 'help' Joanna and to accept that if she was about to make a mistake, then he should leave her to it. Both Joanna and Ron found this arrangement acceptable.

In summary, then, try to understand why you become angry in certain situations and with certain people. Perhaps you are mixing them up with other people. If you are feeling ill, it may be you are imagining that they *are* other people. Secondly, try to see things from their point of view. Try to put yourself in their position and avoid misunderstandings by asking them what they mean when they say something that upsets you. It may be that their intentions are good, but they are not communicating their intentions well enough.

Preparing helpful sentences

If your head is full of negative thoughts, it is difficult to control your anger. In the same way that worrying over something can make things seem worse than they actually are, so too can angry thoughts. It is very difficult to think straight when you are angry. You might realize that you are being unreasonable but not be able to do anything about it. Somehow, it just isn't possible to put a reasonable thought in your mind.

If this is the case, then it makes sense to prepare 'reasonable' sentences that you can say to yourself in order to stop your anger getting out of hand. This technique is specially useful if you have already identified situations that make you angry. You can then enter those situations, having rehearsed 'reasonable' or calming sentences.

Never 'work yourself up' if you know you are about to enter a provocative situation. Instead of thinking of all the bad things that are going to happen, just stop and say something to yourself like: 'Sure, this is going to upset me, but I know I can deal with it.' When you find yourself thinking of all the bad things that are going to happen again, repeat the procedure: stop thinking; repeat your reasonable sentence. Sometimes it's useful to keep a rubber band wrapped around your wrist. When your negative thoughts start to get out of control, pull the band and let it flick against your wrist while you say the word 'stop'. Because the rubber band hurts a bit, this can distract you from your negative thoughts and allow you to think of the more reasonable thought that you prepared earlier.

So, what about when you are actually in a conflict situation? Well, you can do something very similar again. Have a pre-prepared statement that will help you cope, something that is relevant to you. If you are the sort of person who has a tendency to be proud, then prepare a statement like: 'You don't need to prove yourself.' If you think the person who is provoking you is likely to 'shout over' what you are saying, then prepare a statement like: 'There's no point in getting involved here, he simply isn't listening.' If you prepare sentences like this before you are angry, they are more easy to think of when you are in the situation.

Finally, when you leave a difficult situation, don't just sit and go over all the bad things again and again. If you managed to sort the problem out, then reflect on your success. Perhaps you could say something to yourself like: 'Maybe I've been getting upset about this for too long; maybe it wasn't really necessary to get that upset in the first place.' If the problem doesn't get sorted out, then on leaving the situation acknowledge the necessity of practice. You could say something to yourself like: 'OK, I didn't sort out the problem, but with more practice I'll get better at this.' Also, strengthen your resolve to do something constructive about the situation next time around.

Controlling your tension

Anger can get out of control if you get too tense. So try to relax before you enter a provocative situation. If you enter a provocative situation feeling 'laid back', then you will be less easily provoked. You could try doing deep muscle relaxation exercises (see chapter 4) before you enter a provocative situation. However, when you are in that situation and feeling tense, use the *applied relaxation procedure*. Take a deep breath; hold it for a few seconds; then breath out slowly. As you breath out slowly, think of a word like 'relax', 'calm', or 'cool'.

Changing what you do

When we talked about worry earlier, we said that worry was an alarm system that tells you to do something about a problem. The same is true of anger – although perhaps it is a louder alarm! Don't let your anger produce more anger. Stop yourself, and try to solve the problem. Work through the stages that we outlined above in the step by step guide:

- define the problem;
- generate solutions;
- decide which one is likely to be the most helpful;
- put it into action without delay.

A final point to make is that although you might have resolved to be reasonable, the person whom you are in conflict with may not have been so wise. If somebody threatens you, or becomes aggressive, just walk away. Don't turn your back on them. Say that you are sorry, but that you don't think you are getting anywhere, and leave the room. Never use aggression against aggression; it always ends badly.

6
Surviving Schizophrenia

In the previous chapter we mentioned 'hassles', everyday problems that make us feel stressed. If you are a person with schizophrenia, then even the most basic chores of day-to-day living can become a hassle. In this chapter we are going to consider basic life skills, those skills necessary for keeping healthy and for independent living. Although the term 'independent living' is used here, it does not necessarily mean total independence. The level of independence that you achieve will be determined by two factors: first, your own wishes; that is, the degree to which you want to be independent; and second, the severity of your illness; that is, the degree to which you can realistically cope with the problems of day-to-day living. For most people, the level of independence they achieve represents a compromise which is reached by considering both wishes and limitations. We will be looking at a number of areas here: developing good eating habits, keeping out of debt, deciding where to live, and forming relationships. Before considering these specific areas, a few general points should be made.

Independent living

Not so long ago, most psychologists and psychiatrists felt that people with schizophrenia should live in hospitals. They felt that appropriate care could only be provided in a hospital setting. The idea was not to keep people 'locked up', but rather to offer 'asylum', or a place of safety. To some extent there is a lot to be said for this view. For those whose symptoms are severe and persistent, a safe haven is indeed necessary. Further, a minority of people with schizophrenia want to be looked after in a hospital setting. Symptoms may be so distressing that life without hospital care would simply present too great a challenge. However, the vast majority of people with schizophrenia do not need to live in hospitals. Although one or even several periods of hospitalization may be necessary during the course of a lifetime, symptoms are not – on the whole – so severe that hospital care is required all of the time. In fact, the traditional view (often promoted by the media) of 'the institutionalized schizophrenic' is becoming almost a rarity in present-day psychiatry.

It is increasingly recognized that the majority of people with schizophrenia are capable of independent living. This recognition has been more readily accepted against a background of changing attitudes towards people with disabilities of any kind. These changing attitudes have had a considerable influence on the way in which health care is provided. Over the past ten years, there has been a steady trend, favouring the development of community-based services (e.g. hostels and day centres) as opposed to hospital services (e.g. larger wards). However, these changes have not 'just happened' spontaneously; they have been prompted by a number of relatively new ideas.

The right to lead a 'normal' life

It has been suggested that people with disabilities have a right to lead as 'normal' a life as is possible, accepting, of course, any limitations. Although it is difficult to say what is and what isn't 'normal', for our purposes 'normal' means 'ordinary', or 'usual'. Put in a slightly different way, a disability should not restrict the exercise of an individual's basic human rights. That means things like: the right to choose what to eat and when to eat it; the right to choose when to get up in the morning, and when to go to bed; the right to decide what clothes you want to wear; the right to spend your own money. All these basic rights, and many more, are taken for granted by most people. However, for many years, these very basic rights were not considered the prerogative of those suffering with a mental illness. This was largely because people suffering from mental illnesses were usually cared for in 'asylums'. Although many of these provided a high standard of care, the hospital setting is by necessity regimented, restricting opportunities for individuals to make decisions for themselves. Clearly, it is unrealistic to expect a hospital to cater for everyone's individual needs. In order to exercise basic human rights, an individual must achieve at least some degree of independence.

Of course, independent living is a risky business. For someone with schizophrenia, living a normal life can be fraught with problems. However, that risk must be looked at together with the benefits of independent living. Most people who have chosen to live more independent lives say that they feel happier doing so. For example, they often report increased self-esteem. Independent living also reduces the differences that exist between those who are said to have a disability and those who haven't. If you are living the same kind of life as everyone else (e.g. living in a flat, doing your own shopping and buying your own clothes) then you are less likely to see yourself as someone who doesn't fit in. More importantly, others too are less likely to see you as someone who is different. Although independence means taking some risks, taking those risks will increase your sense of self-worth and allow you to retain your dignity.

Ideas about the desirability of independent living have had a dramatic effect on health care. People with schizophrenia are now usually encouraged to take as much responsibility for their own lives as is possible. This should not mean that they are abandoned and left to their own devices. It simply means that they are given as much support as is necessary to enable them to exercise their basic human rights and make their own decisions. In an effort to encourage independent living more and more people with schizophrenia are given accommodation in ordinary houses rather than hospitals. Such accommodation is available (albeit more rarely than is desirable) as part of an existing community care programme.

Even for those living at home and requiring considerable support from their families, the notion of independence is still relevant. It is still possible for such individuals to take a more active role in determining what happens to them. Further, at least some responsibilities (e.g. budgeting) can be taken on without taking serious risks.

Setting modest goals

An important key to success in any endeavour is to recognize one's limitations, as we have already mentioned with respect to work. This principle should be one that you apply to all areas of life: never take on too much. If you want to live more independently, then set realistic goals that you can reach in small stages. For example, if you want to be able to cook for yourself, and at present you are not cooking anything, don't try to go from one extreme to the other. If you try to cook every meal, this might prove to be too demanding. You might then be tempted to give up, and you will inevitably feel disappointed. Such disappointments may discourage you from trying again.

In acquiring or developing any new skill the best incentive is success, however small. If you are succeeding, then you are more likely to continue. So when planning to acquire new skills, set modest and realistic goals. Give yourself a really good chance of succeeding.

Looking after yourself

Coping with life is so much easier if you feel good. This means feeling good about yourself, as well as feeling fit and healthy. Attempting to live a more independent life will almost certainly make you feel better about yourself. However, you should also aim to keep physically fit. This means eating sensibly, getting enough sleep, and if possible exercising regularly. The subject of sleep is covered in chapter 7, so for the moment, let's just say that keeping regular hours is important.

Appearance and personal hygeine

Be aware of the way you look. You don't have to look great, simply clean and tidy; so, take care of your personal hygeine. If you can, try to take at least one bath or shower a day, and be sure to use an underarm deodorant. Get into the habit of cleaning your teeth every morning and evening (and, if you are home all day, after meals). There's no simple rule for washing hair, because different kinds of hair require different amounts of washing; about once every three days is probably OK if your hair doesn't get too greasy. Also, watch out for dandruff. If you do get dandruff, try to buy an anti-dandruff shampoo. Your local chemist will be able to advise you if you aren't sure which of the commercial brands is appropriate. Finally, try to keep your clothes clean. If you can't afford to have clothes dry cleaned, then make sure you wash them regularly by hand, in a washing machine at home, or at the local launderette.

Personal hygeine is very important. It isn't just a chore, it's a statement about self-respect. So respect yourself. Try to monitor how you look by getting into the habit of using mirrors; if you find it difficult to judge how you're looking, then don't be frightened to ask for advice.

Keeping fit

If you can, try to get regular exercise. Exercise can be either formal or informal. Informal exercise can be something like ending a bus journey one stop early and walking the remainder, or using stairs instead of a lift. The idea is simply to make your body work that little bit harder, whenever an opportunity arises. Formal exercise is more organized. It involves doing something like jogging, swimming, or having a game of tennis, and requires more effort. You may need special equipment (e.g. running shoes), or need to book up in advance (e.g. reserving a tennis court). Ideally, you could do a little of both types of exercise. Maybe you could try to be a little more energetic on a day-to-day basis, as well as arranging some formal exercise at least once a week. If you attend a day centre, there will probably be a fitness or aerobics class run on a regular basis. Why not try one out?

If you have a tendency to put on weight, and you are not happy with this, then being more active will certainly help you to lose weight. Exercise builds up your muscle tissue and may increase your rate of metabolism. This means that you will be burning up calories faster, even when you aren't exercising. Of course, the fact that you are exercising in the first place means that you will be burning up more calories than you would do otherwise. In addition, some people find that they eat less after they have been exercising.

Although exercise can help you lose weight, the best reason for doing exercise is to help stay physically healthy. People who exercise regularly tend to get fewer physical illnesses than those who don't. There is even some evidence to suggest that regular exercise helps psychological problems. For example, there have been a few studies showing that people who exercise regularly get less depressed than people who never exercise at all. So try to keep fit if you can.

Eating sensibly

Try to eat regular meals. This usually means breakfast in the morning, a meal around mid-day, and another meal in the early part of the evening. If you live on your own, it is very important that you eat the right kind of foods. This usually means putting a little effort into preparing meals. There are many good cookbooks available and most are relatively easy to understand. A few cookbooks that contain 'healthy' recipes are recommended at the end of this chapter. If you don't think you're up to reading and preparing recipes, then you might be better off just trying to follow these rough and easy guidelines:

- Try to eat fewer fatty foods. This means things like fried foods, full-fat milk and cheese.
- Try to eat less sugar. This means things like sweets, chocolate, biscuits and cakes.
- Eat more fibre. This means things like brown bread, wholemeal pasta and high fibre breakfast cereals.
- Eat more fresh fruit, salads and vegetables.
- As a general rule, try to reduce the amount of packaged food you eat, and try to eat more fresh food.

You don't have to cut out all the things that you enjoy to be healthy. Just follow the broad guidelines given above as well as you can.

Morris

Morris had spent three months in hospital after an illness which involved delusional beliefs about being a great religious leader. After discharge, he took three months off work, and was then able to return to his job as a civil servant. Although things were going well in general, he complained of tiredness and found doing household chores rather difficult. The one that he found most difficult was cooking. He hadn't really cooked that much before going into hospital, and he simply didn't know where to begin. Most evenings, when he got back from work, he would go to his local chinese take-away and buy himself something like fried rice and chicken chow mein.

Over a period of about three months, Morris began to put on quite a bit of weight, which made him feel bad about himself. He began to get a little depressed about his appearance, and this depression made him vulnerable to some distressing ideas. For example, he began to think that he was being punished, and that he deserved to die. He was also spending far too much money on his take-away meals. Luckily, he was still being seen as an out-patient at a hospital, and visited a therapist about once a month. His therapist suggested that if he lost some weight, he might feel better about himself and be less depressed. Morris agreed, but said that he didn't know how to. His therapist told him to go swimming at least once a week, and to begin thinking about cooking at home. Morris was able to go swimming once a week, but somehow couldn't get to grips with cooking. Next time he saw his therapist, Morris discussed a simple menu for one day only. This involved the following:

Breakfast

Bran flakes with semi-skimmed milk.
A glass of orange juice.

Lunch

A tuna fish sandwich made with brown bread and virtually fat-free margarine. Followed by 2 apples.

Evening meal

Wholemeal pasta, made with a jar of ready-made tomato and mushroom sauce.
A low calorie strawberry yoghurt.

In addition, he was allowed fresh fruit snacks if he got really hungry between meals.

Morris wrote down the menu, and on his way home bought all the necessary items. The next day was Saturday and everything went to plan. When Morris saw his therapist again, he asked for another simple menu; the therapist obliged with three, and told him to try each one on every Saturday up to his next appointment. Morris found these menus as easy to prepare as the first and was sufficiently inspired to invest in a wholefood cookbook.

Three months later, Morris had lost two stone in weight. He was feeling better about himself, and only visited his local Chinese take-away about once a week. He no longer had ideas about being punished. He had got into the habit of planning meals and went shopping every Saturday morning. His cookbook was particularly useful when it came to preparing a shopping list. In addition, he carried on swimming once a week, and had started playing squash once a fortnight with a friend from work.

Kicking bad habits

If you want to keep healthy, then it might be worth thinking about the amount of alcohol you drink and the number of cigarettes you smoke. If possible, cut out drinking and smoking altogether. If you can't give up smoking and drinking, then have a go at reducing cigarettes and alcohol by at least fifty per cent. Your doctor will be more than willing to give you advice on how to cut down. Finally, if you take illegal drugs like marijuana, stop immediately. Marijuana can make the symptoms of schizophrenia much worse. In addition, there is some evidence to suggest that marijuana can increase the likelihood of symptoms re-emerging, even if you are feeling better. Finally, marijuana is an illegal drug and possession can lead to prosecution and imprisonment.

Housing

If you have had a period of illness in hospital, or at home, and would like to live more independently, there are a number of accommodation options. It is best to discuss these options with a social worker. Most hospital or community care teams include a social worker who will have expert knowledge of this area.

Supported housing provides an intermediate step between living in hospital and living in your own place. This usually means living in a hostel or something called a half-way house. This type of accommodation allows you to come and go as you please, and you are expected to cook for yourself and generally look after yourself. However, the house will have frequent visits from health professionals, or have a kind of caretaker living in. In the event of a problem arising these people can be consulted.

Other residents of such houses are often people who have had a period of mental illness and are also trying to get used to independent living. Hostels and half-way houses provide an ideal opportunity to test out living skills with minimal risk.

Money

Many people with schizophrenia have enormous difficulty managing their personal finances. This is especially true for those who are not working and are dependent on small social security payments. Many complain that long before the next payment is due, the previous payment has been spent. If you find that you are constantly overspending, or getting into debt, the following system might be useful.

First, work out how much money you can afford to spend on a daily basis. If you live in rented accommodation, or have to pay any bills, then work out your daily spending allowance after putting an appropriate sum aside. Next, label a series of jars with the days of the week on each: Monday, Tuesday, Wednesday, Thursday, Friday, Saturday, Sunday. Place your daily allowance in each, and only spend what you are allowed for each day. It is much easier to keep track of your spending if you employ such a system. If, for example, you find that by midday on Monday, your Monday jar is empty, then you know not to spend any more that day!

If your social security money is for a whole month, then you can still operate the jar system. You simply put three weeks' money aside, and only use the jars for the first week's payment. At the end of week one, you retrieve the second week's money, and so on. Before using this system, it's probably a good idea to sit down with someone and work out exactly how much spending money you have. It is usually less than you think.

Sex and relationships

For most people with schizophrenia, the possibility of forming an intimate relationship is only given serious consideration after the more severe symptoms of the illness have subsided. As a rule, intimacy is difficult to maintain, even when symptoms are of moderate severity. However, as suggested earlier, symptoms often improve after hospital care. After a period of relatively good health, a person who has recovered from his or her symptoms may become more aware of sexual feelings and desire an intimate relationship.

In general, people find sex far more satisfying if it is experienced as part of a loving relationship. Although some people say that they enjoy sex in the absence of love and closeness, the vast majority prefer lovemaking to be meaningful. Within a loving relationship, sex becomes more than just physical contact, albeit pleasurable, and becomes instead a means of expressing and communicating feelings. Casual sex, on the other hand, is often disappointing. By casual sex, we mean sex with someone whom you do not know very well. In the absence of a relationship, sexual intercourse may only occur once with that particular person. When this happens, it is often described as 'a one-night stand'. Although casual sex can be exciting, people tend to report feeling unhappy or dissatisfied after the event. During the course of a long-term relationship, it is possible to develop a rapport with one's partner. It is easier to ask him or her to do things to you that you find pleasurable. In addition, you have sufficient time in which to discover what your partner likes.

Only entertain the idea of a relationship if you are feeling OK. If you aren't confident that your symptoms have subsided, then wait. It is much better to start a relationship on a secure footing. If you meet somebody whom you like, and you want to sleep with them, it's probably a good idea to let them know about your illness first. If they learn that you have experienced symptoms associated with schizophrenia, and find that difficult to accept, then they might decide they do not want to continue the relationship. If you have already formed an intimate attachment and this happens, you will inevitably feel hurt and disappointed. So, try to be honest, and let your prospective partner know about your schizophrenia. Similarly, it would only be fair for your partner to be equally honest with you about any problems which they might have.

If you tell someone whom you like about your symptoms, and they decide that they do not want a relationship with you, then it is unlikely that the relationship would have been successful anyway. If someone cannot accept you after just hearing about your symptoms, then, should these symptoms occur again, such a person is likely to abandon the relationship. Clearly, this would cause you a great deal of pain and distress.

When choosing a partner, make sure that they are supportive, and care about you. Similarly, make sure that you are prepared to support and care for them. Relationships are between two people, and both must be prepared to give.

Safe sex

If you meet someone whom you like and decide that you would like to sleep with them, always use a condom. A condom is a rubber sheath that covers the man's penis during intercourse. You can buy them in any chemist or get them from vending machines which are sometimes located in men's toilets. Some women's toilets also have these machines now.

The condom was originally used to stop unwanted pregnancy. The rubber prevents the man's semen (also called spunk, ejaculate, or cum) from getting into the .woman's body. However, the condom now has a much more important function: to stop the spread of the Human Immunodeficiency Virus, otherwise known as HIV. If you are infected with HIV, you may go on to develop Acquired Immune Deficiency Syndrome, otherwise known as AIDS. AIDS is a lethal illness. If you develop AIDS, you will die.

You cannot get HIV from ordinary mouth to mouth kissing. Although it is theoretically possible, there are no case reports of HIV having been transmitted in this way. Engaging in oral sex is a potentially greater risk. This means kissing, sucking, or licking another person's genitals. However, there is some debate as to how risky oral sex is. Some experts have suggested that it is no more risky than kissing, but it is probably too early to say for sure.

Sexual intercourse, on the other hand, is a high-risk behaviour. If you have penetrative sex with someone who has the HIV virus, and do not use a condom, you too can become infected. It does not matter if they are male or female. If you are a man, always use a condom. If you are a woman, make sure that your partner is wearing a condom before intercourse. Many people become frightened at the mere mention of AIDS. However, you should not let 'fear of AIDS' stop you from forming relationships. If you use a condom, then risks are substantially reduced.

Some men find it difficult to sustain an erection (a hard penis) while using a condom. Consequently, sex can become less satisfying. If you decide that you want to stay with your partner, and you also want to stop using condoms, then you should go for an HIV test. You can discuss the HIV test with your doctor. A sample of blood is taken, from which doctors can tell whether the infection is present. If you are both clear, then you can have intercourse without using a condom. However, you will of course have to use some other form of contraceptive if you do not want to have a baby. The most likely candidate is something called the contraceptive pill. This is a small pill taken every day by women. Alternatively, an injection can be given once a month. The injection is probably the better idea, as it is relatively easy to forget to take the pill. Also, the pill might not be effective if you are sick after taking it.

A final warning

Unfortunately, people with schizophrenia, especially women, are often vulnerable when living in the community. Sadly, there are certain individuals who befriend women who suffer from mental illness for only one reason: to take advantage of them. This taking advantage usually involves manipulating them in some way so that they agree to having sexual intercourse. When people with schizophrenia are not feeling well, their judgement can be seriously impaired. An individual may agree to sexual intercourse without really fully understanding the situation and/or its consequences. At worse, unscrupulous individuals have been known to rape women with schizophrenia, feeling confident that the crime will not be reported or that the evidence of someone with schizophrenia will not be taken seriously by the police.

If you are a woman with a recurrent illness, and living alone in the community, introduce any new friends to your social worker. If a new friend is reluctant to meet any of the health professionals you have contact with, then it would be advisable to clarify the nature of your relationship with them. Perhaps you could talk it over with your doctor or social worker first.

'Healthy' cookbooks

Sarah Brown, *Healthy Living Cookbook*, Dorling Kindersley 1985.
Rose Elliot, *The New Simply Delicious*, Fontana/Collins 1989.
More Vegetarian Cuisine, edited by Paula Borton and Jenny Mann, Fontana/Collins 1988.

7

Dealing with Insomnia

Sleep is an important part of everybody's life; we all need sleep to be healthy. When an individual is having difficulty getting to sleep, the problem is called insomnia, and in this chapter we will be considering ways of dealing with it. However, before making any suggestions it is necessary to make a few comments about those individuals who need less sleep than others.

You don't have to sleep all night

Many people worry about not getting enough sleep because they have heard that it is necessary to have at least eight hours sleep a night. Although many people do require eight hours sleep every night, many others don't. Everybody is different and you may be someone who simply doesn't need a lot of sleep. Some people can get away with as little as three or four hours. If you feel OK sleeping less than everybody else, then there's no need to see it as a sleep problem. Although, if you do need less sleep than everybody else, you might develop problems of a rather different kind. If, for example, you have been up half the night, feeling lonely and bored, you may feel depressed. It's likely that with nothing to do, your worries and concerns will seem worse than they actually are.

One of the best ways to stop this happening is to plan things to do in your extra time. Instead of just sitting and waiting for sleep, try to work out a routine. You don't have to do this for the whole week; just a few days would do to start with. Here's an example:

MONDAY:	12.00 midnight until 12.30 a.m.	Do ironing
	12.30 until 1.30 a.m.	Listen to 'phone in' on the radio
	1.30 until 2.00 a.m.	Listen to music
	2.00 until 2.15 a.m.	Make a hot drink
	2.30 a.m.	Go to bed
TUESDAY:	12.00 midnight until 12.30 a.m.	Tidy my bedroom
	12.30 until 1.00 a.m.	Watch TV
	1.00 until 1.30 a.m.	Plan tomorow's shopping

1.30 until 2.00 a.m.	Do some relaxation exercises
2.00 until 2.30 a.m.	Look at the paper
2.30 a.m.	Go to bed

If you find that planning for a few days a week makes your night-time easier to cope with, then put more effort into developing a regular routine throughout the week. There might be particular programmes on TV or the radio that you enjoy and are able to catch more often. In addition, if you plan well, many of the things that you never get around to doing during the day might be more easily accomplished during the night. Things that you usually view as chores might be more readily viewed as exercises that help you to wind down; for example, doing your ironing. Ironing is a particularly good example, as it is undemanding and repetitive, and undemanding and repetitive tasks are usually very relaxing.

If you find that loneliness is a problem, you could ask your local day centre if anybody in your area is providing 24-hour cover. This means that someone is by a telephone in order to take care of an emergency should it arise. You might be able to work out an arrangement whereby you are allowed to call the number for a chat if you are feeling particularly lonely or depressed in the middle of the night. A short phone call would probably be permissible. Just knowing that someone is there if you really need them can be very reassuring.

In summary, if you don't need as much sleep as everybody else, try to use the extra time you have profitably. Try not to worry about 'getting enough' sleep; you may not need it. There is nothing wrong with needing less sleep than others. Finally, ask your doctor or someone at your local community centre if it's OK to make late-night calls for a short chat, if you think you will find that helpful or reassuring.

Avoid using drugs and alcohol

Many people who can't get to sleep at night ask their doctors for drugs to help them. Although drugs can be useful in the short term, it is probably better to try to cope without them. Many 'sleeping pills' begin to lose their sedative effect when taken for a long time. When this happens, it is very easy to slip into the habit of taking more than the number prescribed by your doctor. After increasing the dosage your body might get used to higher levels of the drug, and again the result might be that they are less effective. So treat sleeping pills with caution; it is not a bad thing to take them every now and again, but they are not really a satisfactory solution to long-term sleeping difficulties.

Another common – and ultimately unhelpful – thing that people take to help sleep is alcohol. Although drinking alcohol can help you to relax, the costs of using alcohol easily outnumber the benefits. Firstly, alcohol has been known to make the symptoms of schizophrenia worse. Therefore, any unnecessary drinking is ill advised. Secondly, alcohol-assisted sleep can be quite different from ordinary sleep. You may find that after going to sleep easily, you wake up a few hours later and can't get back to sleep again. This is probably because alcohol affects the balance of chemicals in your body necessary for a good night's sleep. At a more mundane level, it is likely that your sleep will be interrupted by having to get up and visit the toilet! Finally, drinking too much before bedtime will more than likely result in a headache (a 'hangover') the following morning.

Some people with schizophrenia attempt to get a better night's sleep by using illegal street drugs, in particular marijuana. The drug is usually offered by someone trying to be 'helpful', often a friend rather than a 'drug-pusher'. This drug does indeed help people to sleep. As well as being illegal it is likely to increase the severity of schizophrenic symptoms. If you suffer from schizophrenia and someone offers you marijuana, refuse it; it can be extremely dangerous.

Have I got a sleep problem?

When people suggest that they have a sleep problem they usually mean one or all of the following:

a) they can't get to sleep at night;
b) they find they wake up several times during the night;
c) they wake up too early in the morning and can't get back to sleep again.

In addition, they complain that when they do sleep they wake up feeling unrefreshed. Furthermore, they continue to feel tired throughout the day. If these things apply to you, then it is possible that you are suffering from insomnia. It is important to say at this point that general tiredness can be caused by the drugs that are used to treat schizophrenia. So if you have just started taking neuroleptic medication, discuss your tiredness with your doctor. A change of medication may be all that is necessary. On the other hand, it may be that you are having problems with sleeping, and this is making the tiredness caused by medication worse.

A further point to consider is that early-morning waking is a symptom of depression. The subject of depression is really beyond the brief of this book. If you feel very depressed, and are consistently waking up early in the morning, then it is probably best to discuss this with your doctor. Again, he or she might advise a change in medication.

We have suggested so far that you might find it difficult getting to sleep at nights, and further the sleep that you have might not be refreshing. If you are trying to cope with difficult and frightening symptoms, then you will need to make the most of your sleep. It will be far easier to use many of the suggestions mentioned in this book if you are not feeling exhausted all the time.

In the following sections, a number of suggestions are made to help you get a better night's sleep. In addition, you are also advised of several things that you shouldn't do. Some of the points are general, others are more specific.

How to get a better night's sleep

Don't sleep on your problems; solve them

One of the main causes of insomnia is worry. If you go to bed and worry about your problems, it is going to be very difficult to go to sleep. It is also likely that you will wake up early in the morning. Although it is possible to improve your sleep by using some of the techniques suggested in this chapter, these techniques will be much more effective if you solve the problems that are making you worry in the first place. You will find more about worry and how to deal with it in chapter 6. Put very simply, if you address the problems that make you worry, then you will worry less and get a better night's sleep.

Don't keep irregular hours

If you do not have a job, or are attending a centre that doesn't open until late in the day, then there is very little reason to get up in the morning, or, for that matter, keep the same hours as everyone else. Many people with schizophrenia find that they go to bed later and later. Because they go to bed later, they also get up later as well. Eventually, if things go too far, they can end up going to sleep when everybody else is waking up; their hours become so irregular they are the exact opposite of everybody else's. Clearly, this is undesirable; it can make an individual feel very isolated and limit opportunities to make use of services provided in the community.

Most people have a tendency to go to bed later and later each night if left to their own devices. The reasons for this phenomenon are unclear, but it seems that this tendency is a normal one. For example, people tend to go to bed later on Saturday night because they don't have to get up to go to work on Sunday morning. On Sunday morning, they might stay in bed until quite late. When Sunday night comes, it will probably be quite difficult to go to sleep because they stayed in bed for most of Sunday morning. However, because of work on Monday, they will have to get up early. As a result of this, they may only get about six hours sleep. This means that getting to sleep on Monday night will be a little easier. In this way, the tendency towards going to bed later and later is stopped.

Even if you don't have to get up in the mornings, try to get up at the same time. If you over-sleep in the mornings, you may find that this makes sleep in the evenings more difficult. So perhaps you could get into the habit of waking at 7.30 each morning by setting a bedside alarm; this will stop the natural tendency to go to bed later and later each night.

Avoid taking day-time naps

If you sleep for most of the morning, it will be difficult to sleep at night. You simply won't need the sleep. Similarly, if you have got into the habit of taking day-time naps, this will make sleep in the evening more difficult. Breaking this unhelpful habit is relatively easy. When you feel tired during the day, do something to wake yourself up. Take a brisk walk, or do something that requires other activity. Don't sit down and say to yourself, 'I shouldn't go to sleep'. Get up and move around. It's far harder to drift off to sleep when you are standing up than sitting down!

Drink less coffee, especially before bedtime

Coffee ordinarily contains the drug caffeine, which is likely to stop you from getting a good night's sleep. If you drink too much coffee, you can feel restless, nervous and agitated, none of which are compatible with sleep and sleeping. You don't have to give up coffee entirely. You might, for example, drink coffee in the daytime but not have any after 6.00 p.m. Alternatively, you could buy decaffeinated coffee (coffee with the caffeine taken out), instead. Coffee, like alcohol, can make you want to go to the toilet more frequently than usual. So remember, even if we ignore its direct effect on sleep, drinking too much coffee before bedtime is likely to cause an interrupted night.

Reduce activity levels before going to bed

When you have been active, it takes a little time to wind-down. If you have been out with friends, or have been exercising, or have simply been doing strenuous work about the house, you may find sleep difficult. Always allow two or three hours in which to wind down, or even better avoid being too active before bedtime altogether.

Challenge upsetting thoughts about personal safety

Many people with schizophrenia suffer from thoughts about persecution or harm. These thoughts can become particularly bothersome at night, as most people recognize they are very vulnerable when asleep and feel more frightened when it is dark. Remember, it's very easy to let small fears grow if they are unchallenged. If you get frightening thoughts like, 'There's someone outside in the garden', don't just accept the thought, go to the window and have a look. Often this is all it takes to allay such a fear. Finally, you might get into the habit of checking that everything is safe and secure: the locks on the windows and doors, etc. Although not absolutely necessary, such a routine might help you feel safer and assist in achieving restful sleep.

Using relaxation

As suggested above, it is very difficult to get to sleep if you are either 'wound up' or worried. Therefore, it is important to get into a relaxed state before attempting sleep. You can try to relax informally by, for example, having a hot bath or listening to music. Alternatively, you could try a more formal approach and use the relaxation exercises described in chapter 3. Just to remind you, this involves tensing and relaxing various muscle groups all over your body. Of course, there's nothing stopping you from winding down for thirty minutes or so by listening to music, or doing whatever you find calming, before undertaking your more formal relaxation exercises.

Only go to bed when you're tired

Another way of dealing with your insomnia is only to go to bed when you feel tired. If you go to bed and find that you are not going to sleep, don't just lie there tossing and turning, get up and do something. Never lie in bed for more than half an hour while awake.

If you live in a bedsit, then get out of bed, sit in a comfortable chair and read or listen to the radio. If you live somewhere with other rooms in addition to your bedroom, then go and sit in another room. When you begin to feel sleepy, go back to bed. On no account go to sleep in a chair or wherever you are sitting. If you still can't get to sleep, get up again.

The reason for doing this is to train yourself to associate bed with sleeping. The stronger the association, the easier it will be to get to sleep. The more time you spend in bed doing things other than sleeping, the weaker the association will be. So try to use your bed for sleeping, and nothing else.

Even if you spend much of the night getting up and doing other things, you must still get up at whatever time you have decided marks the beginning of your day. If you set the alarm for 7.30 a.m. and the alarm goes off, then you must get up and stay up until bedtime. Remember, even if you feel really tired during the day, you must stay awake and avoid taking naps.

Hot milky drinks and herb tea

There are many adverts that suggest that making a hot milky drink before bedtime helps people to sleep. We are referring here to products like cocoa (or drinking chocolate), Horlicks and Ovaltine. For once the advertisers are telling the truth. It does seem to be the case that hot milky drinks do help people get to sleep. Although they are not, by any means, a cure for insomnia, you might find that having a hot milky drink just before bedtime helps you to wind down.

Although little research has been conducted into herb teas, a number of people have suggested that these can be helpful too. Perhaps the most common tea used for sleep problems is camomile tea. You can get camomile tea bags in most health food shops. Unlike ordinary tea, camomile tea is not usually taken with milk. You also have to leave herb tea bags in the cup for a little while longer than ordinary tea bags. Even though there isn't a great deal of scientific evidence suggesting that they are effective, you could try drinking camomile tea by way of an experiment to see if it works for you.

Coping with noise

Many people can't get to sleep because they live in places that are simply too noisy: you may have noisy neighbours, or you may live near a busy road, and the constant sound of traffic may make sleep very difficult. A simple way of reducing noise is to use ear plugs.

These are quite cheap and most chemists sell them. The most effective ear plugs are those made of wax. You work the wax with your fingers until it becomes soft and warm. You can then press the wax into your ears, sealing up the entrances. After doing this you will find that most of the sound that normally disturbs you is blocked out. You might still be able to feel sound vibrations when noise is particularly loud, but this shouldn't bother you too much. Although sleeping with ear plugs in might feel a little uncomfortable at first, it is worth persevering. Most people soon get used to them.

Summary

Let's summarize some of the information in this chapter. Here are ten points to consider.

1 If you are having trouble sleeping at night, then this may be because you are someone who doesn't need a great deal of sleep. If this is the case, then try not to worry about being 'different', and plan some relaxing or constructive activities in your extra hours to avoid boredom.

2 You have a genuine sleep problem if you feel unrefreshed in the morning and tired in the day after experiencing one or more of the following:
   a) difficulty getting to sleep at night;
   b) waking up several times during the night;
   c) waking up very early in the morning, and not being able to get back to sleep.

   Some of these symptoms might be due to your medication. Therefore a discussion with your doctor is advised.

3 If your worries keep you awake at night, then try to solve the problems that are causing you to worry in the first place.

4 Never use alcohol or illegal drugs to help you to get to sleep. If you must take something to help you sleep in the evenings, then a hot milky drink or camomile tea are recommended.

5 Avoid drinking coffee in the evenings, or, even better, cut it out altogether or just drink decaffeinated coffee.

6 Don't keep irregular hours. Try to get up at the same time every morning, and don't sleep during the day.

7 Don't exercise or do strenuous work before going to bed. Always spend some time relaxing before attempting to sleep.

8 Relaxation exercises can help you to get to sleep once you are in bed.

9 Don't lie in your bed awake. If you can't get to sleep, it is better to get up and do something else until you feel tired again. Only then should you go to bed.

10 Make sure that your house is secure if it makes you feel safer. Use ear plugs if you are troubled by noise.

8
Knowing Your Rights

The theme of this book has been to demonstrate the practical roles which clinician, carer and client can all have in surviving the illness of schizophrenia. As such it provides one source of information for people to draw on as they are involved in the development of their own individual treatment programme. Many of the ideas presented will be familiar to professionals whom you will encounter in mental health services, others will not. In a busy clinical practice the professional staff may not always be able to provide the full range of options outlined here and thus may not suggest them. If you are aware of them, however, you can ask to be referred on to people who are able to provide you with the additional services you require as either a supplement or an alternative to the care you are presently receiving. Social workers play a crucial role in organizing support services for people with mental health problems. They can be contacted through a mental health team or by a direct request to the local social services office.

Advocacy

One of the problems that people frequently complain of is the difficulty of ensuring that their voice is heard when they wish to discuss a problem. There can too often be a perception that people are too busy to listen or that problems are not being treated with sufficient seriousness. It is important in these situations to feel that it is possible to contact someone who might be able to help you put forward your point of view. This is known as advocacy. An advocate is someone whose role is to present your point of view in the best way possible to the relevant people. Advocacy has long been used by the trade unions as a method to ensure that employees receive a fair deal from their employers; similarly lawyers are used for much the same purpose in court cases.

In the case of mental health problems there are a range of situations in which an advocate might be used. An advocate can be any competent person whom you trust to help you to present your views. Advocates may be:

1 Mental health professionals

Some day centres and other mental health centres operate a key worker system. This key worker is a qualified mental health professional who works specifically with that individual. Thus when a person needs help or advice with specific problems the key worker serves as the first port of call. If he or she is unable to solve the problem they are likely to function as an advocate for the client. They will do this by presenting the person's problem to the appropriate agency and ensuring that the required action is taken.

Similarly psychologists, doctors, social workers or nurses can act as advocates in supporting clients' applications for benefits or housing provision.

It should be emphasized that mental health professionals will function as advocates in a limited sense. As they are employed by the national health service to do a particular job it will not be within their remit strongly to support the client who wants to do something which they believe in their professional judgement would be detrimental to them.

2 Interested lay people

It can often be helpful to invite along a relative or trusted friend if you are having meetings with health service professionals or with benefits agencies. Often two heads are better than one. Most people do not remember everything that is said in meetings but if you put your heads together then you are likely to get more from it.

3 Another individual with experience of schizophrenia

If you are not currently in contact with any of these groups of people Useful Addresses at the end of this book may be a place to start.

Advocacy training

Advocacy training courses are designed to teach the skills necessary for people to get their point of view across in the most effective manner. This means being able to be involved in meetings about your own care but also possible involvement in committees planning services for people with mental health problems. Meetings of any sort can be stressful for those who are not used to them, for professionals and clients alike. Thus advocacy training can be very helpful in increasing a client's confidence about expressing their views and knowledge about the best places to raise particular issues.

Assertiveness is part of the function of such training. This is not the same as aggressiveness. Assertiveness is about putting your case clearly and not feeling that you have to agree with other people if you know that what they are saying is wrong. This sounds easy, but in fact is not. Most of us tend to prefer not to make a fuss and to get along with people. This is fine in many situations, but is not useful when important decisions or plans are being made. In these situations, especially if the plans apply to you, it is important that your views are made clear.

In general a number of guidelines are helpful before important meetings of any sort:

- Think about the issues that you want to raise. If you find a quiet place and think over what you want to say beforehand it is much easier to order your thoughts than trying to do it 'on the spur of the moment'.
- Write these issues down. Things that seem clear when you are talking with a friend may become muddled if you are in a group of people at a meeting. If you have some simple notes with you you can refer to these to make sure you say what is on your mind.
- Talk to a relative/friend. Tell them what the points are and what you want to say about them. Check that they understand. If they do not it may be that you need to find a different way of saying it so that it is more clear. Once you are sure that they understand, use this wording again when explaining your views in the meeting.

Jenny

Jenny had been attending a day centre for some months. She received medication from the nurse at the day centre which she did not feel was helping her. She tried to talk to her nurse about it but found this very difficult. Each time she brought the subject up her mind went blank and she became frustrated and angry. This sometimes meant that she had to leave the room. Jenny began to attend a skills course that taught assertiveness and advocacy. Following this she tried preparing for her meeting with her nurse beforehand by asking a friend to pretend she was the nurse while Jenny practised describing her problem. Following this preparation Jenny felt more confident in approaching her nurse and this helped her to explain that she felt very tired and dizzy on the medication she was having. As a result the nurse was able to have the medication altered to a lower dosage which did not have these side-effects.

Mental Health Act

This is an Act of Parliament which states what the rights are of mental health professionals and of people with mental illness, including schizophrenia, when it comes to treatment. Treatment for mental illness is usually done on a voluntary basis. There are however times when this is not the case. If someone is ill and is placing their health or their safety and/or other people at significant risk then the Mental Health Act may be used to place them in hospital even against their wishes.

This form of hospital admission is not done lightly and there are controls on both when it can be used and for how long. There are a number of different sections to the Mental Health Act which are relevant to hospital treatment. These are listed below:

Section 2. This allows for the assessment in hospital of someone and is limited to a maximum of 28 days. The admission must be requested by an approved social worker, or by the nearest relative of the person to be admitted. It must also be recommended by two doctors, at least one of whom must be a specialist in mental illness. On admission to hospital the person has the right of appeal, within 14 days, to a mental health review tribunal (see below).

Section 3. This can be for up to six months and allows the hospital to treat the person to whom it is applied. This again must be applied for by an approved social worker, or the person's nearest relative. Recommendation, as above, must come from two doctors, one of whom must be a specialist in mental illness. This compulsory admission requires the following grounds (in the case of mental illness):

1 Patient is suffering from mental illness for which medical treatment in hospital is appropriate.
2 Such treatment is necessary for the health or safety of the patient or for the protection of other persons and cannot be provided without the use of this section.

Both of these conditions have to be met for Section 3 to be employed. The Section is renewable for a fresh period of six months and after that, for a year at a time.

Mike

Mike had his first schizophrenic breakdown when he was 25 years old. He had been working as a printer for eight years and was enjoying the work. He was earning good money and was saving to buy a flat with his girlfriend, Sandra. Quite suddenly he began to believe that his colleagues were planning to kill him. He continued working for some weeks, but refused to eat with his fellow workers, or go out with them after work, in case they tried to harm him. At home he could hear their voices plotting to harm him. He stopped going to work and became more and more obsessed with listening to the voices plotting against him. He became convinced that they had contaminated his food and he stopped eating. His girlfriend and parents realized that he was unwell and tried to get him to see a doctor, but he refused. Gradually he lost weight and became painfully thin. His GP visited on several occasions but Mike would only talk to him through the keyhole. By this time his family and GP were seriously concerned that Mike might actually harm himself as a result of his refusal to eat and his refusal to accept treatment of any sort. He was eventually admitted to a psychiatric hospital against his will under Section 3 of the Mental Health Act, and he was treated immediately with neuroleptic medication. Over several weeks his paranoia reduced and the voices became less prominent. Mike then began to accept this treatment voluntarily and became an informal patient. After two months in hospital he was discharged. He remains on a small dose of medication, but has been able to return to work. Every fortnight he meets with a psychologist to discuss his progress. At times he again feels that he is being persecuted but is able, with support, to challenge these fears quite successfully.

Section 4. Hospital admission for emergency assessment. This is used when there is only one doctor available and the urgency of the situation does not permit waiting for the recommendation of a second doctor. The doctor making the recommendation in this case would usually be the person's GP. Application is again made by nearest relative or approved social worker. This runs for a maximum of 72 hours after which time the person is free to leave hospital if there are at that time insufficient grounds for Section 2 or 3.

Section 5(2). This is used to detain a person who is currently in hospital informally if they are wishing to leave and their condition is such that it is thought necessary to consider applying for a Section 2 or 3 admission. The procedure is carried out by the consultant psychiatrist charged with the person's care, or by another nominated doctor, and the detention lasts for a maximum of 72 hours. A senior nurse may also detain someone under this section of the Act, for up to six hours, in the absence of a doctor.

Section 136. This gives a police constable the right to remove to a 'place of safety' someone who is in a public place and appears to be mentally disturbed and needs care or control. This place of safety will be a mental health centre, a hospital or a police station.

Section 37. This is applied to a person with a mental disorder who has also committed an offence which is punishable by a prison sentence. If the person is sent to hospital under the terms of this Section they fall under the responsibility of the consultant in charge of their care. Like Section 3, this is of six months' duration in the first instance but can be reversed, initially for six months and then yearly.

When the crime is viewed as particularly serious the Crown Court judge may add an additional restriction (Section 41) to the Section 37. This means that the patient has to have the approval of the Home Secretary before obtaining leave, transfer or discharge from hospital. As with other sections the person can apply directly to the Mental Health Review Tribunal. This restriction order can be cancelled by the Home office, but in most cases it remains in place even when the person is discharged from hospital.

Each of the above sections requires the agreement of a number of different health professionals, to ensure that they are not used inappropriately. In addition, the person to whom the section applies may apply to the Mental Health Review Tribunal for their discharge. This is an independent body which hears appeals from patients who feel they should not be under section. Patients may represent themselves or have an advocate or lawyer to present their case for them. The Tribunal will also hear from the medical and social work staff directly involved in the person's care. If they decide that the section is inappropriate they may cancel it immediately or on a specified date in the future.

Mental Health Act officers in psychiatric hospitals provide both clinician and patients with information on their rights under the Mental Health Act. They also provide information on how to go about appealing to the Mental Health Review Tribunal against sections.

Mental health groups

There are an increasing number of groups being set up to provide help and support for people with schizophrenia and their relatives. Some of these will be local bodies which are set up for people in a particular area. In addition there are a number of established nationwide bodies which exist to promote the causes of people with mental health problems and raise awareness of problems in services.

The best known and most well established of the mental health groups is MIND (National Association for Mental Health). This has its national headquarters in London and regional offices throughout the country. They are involved in trying to improve the services for people with all types of mental health problems. In addition to their role in general service provision they offer advice and information to individual carers and people with mental health problems and are involved in patient advocacy (see above).

The National Schizophrenia Fellowship (NSF) is another nationwide body, this dealing particularly with schizophrenia sufferers and their families. Their emphasis is on providing support and respite for the relatives of people with a schizophrenic illness. NSF runs support groups for carers and also Voices, a group for people with schizophrenia. In addition they manage a number of day care services and mental health groups. NSF, like MIND, has regional centres throughout the country.

Schizophrenia a National Emergency (SANE) is a relatively new pressure group aiming to increase funding of relevant research into treatments for schizophrenia. It also runs the SANELINE, a telephone help-line for people with schizophrenia and their families which operates every day, 2pm to midnight.

The Hearing Voices Network is a nationwide organization of user groups. This means that the groups are run by and for people who experience auditory hallucinations. Many of these people will have a psychiatric diagnosis of schizophrenia; others will not have been in contact with psychiatric services. The groups discuss their experiences and methods they have found of living with their voices.

The addresses of these organizations can be found in the following section.

Useful Addresses

Hearing Voices Network
MACC
Swan Buildings
Ancoats
Manchester M4 5JW
Tel: 061–834 9823

MIND (National Association for Mental Health)
22 Harley Street
London W1N 2ED.
Tel: 071–637 0741

National Schizophrenia Fellowship (NSF)
28 Castle Street
Kingston upon Thames
Surrey KT1 1SS.
Tel: 081–547 3937

SANE (Schizophrenia a National Emergency)
199 Old Marylebone Road
London NW1 5QP.
Tel: 071–724 8000

Index